McGRAW-HILL READING

# Grammar

## Grade 3

## Practice Book

McGraw-Hill
School Division
New York          Farmington

# Contents

## Book 3.1/Unit 2: Nature Links

## Book 3.1/Unit 3: Be Creative!

## Book 3.2/Unit 1: Tell Me More

# Book 3.2/Unit 2: Think It Through

# Book 3.2/Unit 3: Turning Points

# What Is a Sentence?

---

- A **sentence** is a group of words that tells a complete thought.
- Every sentence begins with a capital letter.
  Sentence: *My grandfather walked for days.*
  Not a sentence: *Walked for days.*

---

Write **yes** if the words make a sentence. Write **no** if they do not.

1. My grandfather was born in Japan. _____

2. He came to America on a ship. _____

3. He married and lived in California. _____

4. Land of sunlight and sea. _____

5. Homesick for Japan. _____

6. He moved his family to Japan. _____

7. Mountains and rivers of his childhood. _____

8. Laughed with old friends. _____

9. He raised songbirds. _____

10. Missed California. _____

**Extension:** Have students write three sentences about their family.

# Statements and Questions

> - A **statement** is a sentence that tells something. It ends with a period.
> - A **question** is a sentence that asks something. It ends with a question mark.
>   Statement: *My grandfather liked to travel.*
>   Question: *Do you like to travel?*

Write **statement** if the sentence tells something. Write **question** if the sentence asks something. Put the correct end mark at the end of the sentence.

1. My grandfather's ship crossed an ocean _____

2. Have you seen an ocean _____

3. Is an ocean deep _____

4. My grandfather explored America _____

5. He saw huge cities _____

6. Do you know how many people live in cities _____

7. Where is San Francisco Bay _____

8. My grandfather missed Japan _____

9. There are rivers in Japan _____

10. Are there mountains in Japan _____

**Extension:** Have students work in pairs. Ask each student to write a question about the story. Then have them write a statement to answer each other's question.

# Writing Statements and Questions

---

> • A **statement** is a sentence that tells something. It ends with a period.
> • A **question** is a sentence that asks something. It ends with a question mark.
> Statement: *My grandfather liked to travel.*
> Question: *Do you like to travel?*

After each sentence, write **statement** or **question** for the kind of sentence it is. Then write the sentence correctly. Use capital letters and end marks.

1. many people live in cities _____

   _____

2. the cities are run by electricity _____

   _____

3. electricity lights houses and streets _____

   _____

4. what is it like when the electricity goes out _____

   _____

5. if it's at night, the whole city is dark _____

   _____

6. your home seems like a different place _____

   _____

7. has that ever happened to you _____

   _____

8. were you ever in a city with no lights at night _____

   _____

---

**Extension:** Have pairs of students choose a subject and take turns making up statements and questions about it. The student who is listening tells what kind of sentence is given.

# Using Capital Letters and End Marks

> • Every sentence begins with a capital letter.
>
> • A statement ends with a period.
>
> • A question ends with a question mark.

Correct each sentence. Write the capital letter over the small letter.
Add the end mark.

**1.** i think our country is beautiful _____

**2.** would you like to travel across our country _____

**3.** i've never seen a desert _____

**4.** have you ever seen one _____

**5.** a desert is cold at night _____

**6.** is it cold during the day _____

**7.** where are the mountains in our country _____

**8.** some mountains have snow on the top _____

**9.** our country has many rivers _____

**10.** do you live near a river _____

**Extension:** Have pairs of students look through
magazines to find examples of the two kinds of end
marks. Have students copy an example of each.

# Statements and Questions

**A.** Read each group of words. Write **yes** if the group of words forms a sentence. Write **no** if it does not form a sentence.

**1.** I like to visit my grandfather. _____

**2.** Raised warblers and silvereyes. _____

**3.** He could not forget California. _____

**4.** Never returned to California. _____

**B.** Decide if the sentence is a statement or a question. Write your answer on the line.

**5.** My grandfather moved back to Japan _____

**6.** Where did he buy a house _____

**7.** When did his daughter marry _____

**8.** There was a war _____

**9.** After the war, his house was gone _____

**10.** Did Grandfather get another songbird _____

# Statements and Questions

- A sentence is a group of words that tells a complete thought.
- A statement is a sentence that tells something.
- A question is a sentence that asks something.

**Mechanics:**

- Begin every sentence with a capital letter.
- End a statement with a period.
- End a question with a question mark.

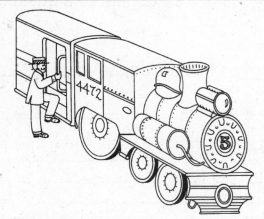

Write each statement or question correctly. Then use the sentences to color the picture.

**1.** my grandfather traveled by train

_____

**2.** he wore a yellow hat and brown coat

_____

**3.** what color was the train

_____

**4.** the train had a black engine

_____

# Commands

> - A **command** is a sentence that tells or asks someone to do something.
> - It ends with a period.
>   Command: *Go to the nurse's office.*

Make each group of words a command. Add a word from the box.
Then write the sentence correctly.

| break | call | raise | sound | stand | take | tell |
|-------|------|-------|-------|-------|------|------|

I. _____ the spelling list home

_____

2. _____ me on the phone

_____

3. _____ me the truth

_____

4. _____ out the word

_____

5. _____ the word into two parts

_____

6. _____ each part

_____

7. _____ your hand

_____

8. _____ in line, please

_____

**Extension:** Have students work in pairs. Tell students
to take turns giving a command for their partner to
act out.

# Exclamations

> • An **exclamation** shows strong feeling.
>
> • It ends with an exclamation mark.
>   Exclamation: What hard work this is!

Make each group of words an exclamation. Add a word from the box.
Then write the sentence correctly.

| great | how | oh | ouch | what | wonderful | wow | watch |

1. _____ no, the spelling bee is in three days

   _____

2. _____ a problem this is

   _____

3. _____ , I think my leg is broken

   _____

4. _____ , Katie won the spelling bee

   _____

5. That's _____

   _____

6. _____ exciting to get a certificate

   _____

7. My certificate said _____ IMAGINATION

   _____

8. _____ out

   _____

**Extension:** Invite students to write two exclamations
about an exciting event in their school.

Book 3.1/Unit 1
**Phoebe and the Spelling Bee**
8

# Commands and Exclamations

---

> • A command tells or asks someone to do something. It ends with a period.
>
> • An exclamation shows strong feeling. It ends with an exclamation point.

After each sentence, write **command** or **exclamation** for the kind of sentence it is. Then write the sentence correctly. Use capital letters and end marks.

**1.** study the words _____

_____

**2.** try to spell each word _____

_____

**3.** what a long list this is _____

_____

**4.** oh no, I think I have the chicken pox _____

_____

**5.** listen to the sounds _____

_____

**6.** how hard this is _____

_____

**7.** please learn the words by Friday _____

_____

**8.** oh dear, Friday is here _____

_____

---

**Extension:** Ask students to write a command and an exclamation about spelling or another school subject.

# Sentence Capitalization and Punctuation

> • Every sentence begins with a capital letter.
>
> • A **command** ends with a period.
>
> • An **exclamation** ends with an exclamation mark.

Proofread the sentences. Write them correctly.

**1.** wow, that's my favorite food

_____

**2.** tell it to me

_____

**3.** what a terrific word that is

_____

**4.** spell your word

_____

**5.** oh no, the word is too long

_____

**6.** i like words that describe animals

_____

**7.** listen to my list

_____

**8.** i'm learning to spell my words

_____

**Extension:** Have students write two commands and two exclamations to tell about some kind of emergency situation.

# Commands and Exclamations

**A.** Find the group of words that is a command. Mark your answer.

1. ⓐ Are you ready?
   ⓑ I'll help you.
   ⓒ Spell the word.

2. ⓐ Spelling is fun.
   ⓑ Listen to me.
   ⓒ Did you study?

3. ⓐ I feel sick.
   ⓑ Go see the nurse.
   ⓒ Where is the nurse?

4. ⓐ Wish me luck.
   ⓑ Today is Friday.
   ⓒ Do you like stories?

**B.** Decide if the sentence is a statement, a command, a question, or an exclamation. Mark your answer.

5. How nervous I am!
   ⓐ statement
   ⓑ command
   ⓒ question
   ⓓ exclamation

6. I folded the paper into an airplane.
   ⓐ statement
   ⓑ command
   ⓒ question
   ⓓ exclamation

7. What a great landing it made!
   ⓐ statement
   ⓑ command
   ⓒ question
   ⓓ exclamation

8. Do it.
   ⓐ statement
   ⓑ command
   ⓒ question
   ⓓ exclamation

# Commands and Exclamations

- A **command** is a sentence that tells someone to do something.
- An **exclamation** shows strong feeling.

**Mechanics:**

- Begin every sentence with a capital letter.
- End a command with a period.
- End an exclamation with an exclamation mark.

Read each group of words aloud. Write the words in order as a sentence.

**1.** study spelling help Phoebe

_____

**2.** her listen to stories

_____

**3.** funny her stories how are

_____

**4.** a story please me tell

_____

**5.** exciting story what an it is

_____

Read the new sentences aloud. Do they make sense?

## Subjects

---

- The **subject** of a sentence is whom or what the sentence is about.
- The subject can be one word or more than one word.
  A wall surrounds the castle.
  *A wall* is the subject.

---

What or whom is the sentence about? Draw a line under the subject.

1. Balloons float in the air.

2. The guard holds a trident.

3. Someone brings a letter for the king.

4. The king reads the message.

5. Bright flowers bloom in the garden.

6. The Great Hall is ready for a party.

7. Amazing animals live in the Opt Zoo.

8. A fire-snorting dragon comes to the castle.

9. Six blocks can become seven blocks.

10. Everyone has fun at the party.

---

**Extension:** Have students work in pairs. Ask each student to write two sentences about a castle. Then tell students to draw a line under the subjects of their partner's sentences. **13**

# Fixing Fragments by Adding Subjects

> • A **sentence fragment** is a group of words that does not express a complete thought.
>
> • Some sentence fragments can be fixed by adding a subject.

Fix each fragment in the first column by adding a subject from the second column. Write the subject.

| # | Fragment | Subjects |
|---|----------|----------|
| 1. | _____ has white lines on it. | Gray dots |
| 2. | _____ disappear from the wall. | A clue |
| 3. | _____ waits for a letter. | The prince |
| 4. | _____ makes the message clear. | The wall |
| 5. | _____ hang on the wall. | A sign |
| 6. | _____ fishes with his new rod. | The king |
| 7. | _____ picks flowers. | Two pictures |
| 8. | _____ are black and white. | Many kites |
| 9. | _____ points the way to the zoo. | Flower centers |
| 10. | _____ float in the air. | The princess |

**Extension:** Invite students to take turns finding subjects from the story Opt: An Illusionary Tale. Then have them make a sentence about each subject.

# Writing Subjects to Complete Sentences

> • Every sentence has a subject.
>
> • The subject of a sentence tells what or whom the sentence is about.

Add a subject to each group of words. Write the sentence.

1. _____ is a land of surprises.

_____

2. _____ has red and blue tape on it.

_____

3. _____ may be taller than the queen.

_____

4. _____ has a shade on it.

_____

5. _____ catches a fish.

_____

6. _____ looks in the mirror.

_____

7. _____ stops by the sign.

_____

8. _____ marches up the stairs of the tower.

_____

**Extension:** Have one group of students write subjects about the Prince's party. Have another group write predicates. Invite students to match subjects and predicates to make sentences about the Prince's party.

# Letter Punctuation and Capitalization

- Begin the greeting and closing in a letter with a capital letter.
- Use a comma after the greeting and the closing in a letter.
- Use a comma between the names of a city and a state.
- Use a comma between the day and year in a date.

Proofread the letter. Correct five capitalization mistakes. Add five missing commas.

January 15 2000

123 main Street
Hewlett  NY 11557

Kim chan
456 Mott street
New York  NY 10010

dear Kim

Your letter came today. It is so good to hear from you. I'm glad to know you're having fun in your new school.

We also read the story about Opt last week. I liked it. The story pictures are puzzles. What fun they are!

Please let me know when you can come and visit.

your friend

Pat

## Subjects

**A.** Write the subject of each sentence.

**1.** The queen dusts the room. _____

**2.** Four banners hang from the ceiling. _____

**3.** The Opt sign has lines on it. _____

**4.** A guest arrives in Opt. _____

**B.** Choose a subject from the box that best completes each sentence. Write it on the line.

| A guard | Opt | A messenger | The castle |
|---------|-----|-------------|------------|

**5.** _____ is an unusual place.

**6.** _____ is surrounded by a wall.

**7.** _____ stands in front of the castle.

**8.** _____ brings a letter.

## Subjects

---

• The subject of a sentence tells what or whom the sentence is about.

**Mechanics:**

• Begin every sentence with a capital letter.

• End every sentence with a special mark.

Look at the picture. Read the paragraph and look at the underlined parts. What should you do to correct each part? Rewrite the sentences on the lines.

    I just read about Opt. (1) <u>is fun to read</u>.  (2) <u>every page has a puzzle</u> (3) <u>do you like puzzles</u> The puzzle about the king and queen is my favorite. Who is taller? (4)<u>what a surprise to find out they are the same</u>

_____

_____

_____

_____

# Predicates

---

- Every sentence has two parts.
- Every sentence has a predicate.
- The **predicate** of a sentence tells what the subject does or is.
  Two boys go to the toy store.
  The predicate is <u>go to the toy store.</u>

---

Which word or words tell what the subject does or is? Draw a line under the predicate.

1. The boys talk with the store manager.

2. They buy a box of baseballs.

3. The friends count forty-eight balls.

4. Dusty Field is a famous baseball player.

5. People stand in line for Dusty's autograph.

6. The boys sell baseballs to the kids.

7. Dusty signs the baseballs.

8. Austin is a friend of the boys.

9. Austin misses Dusty Field.

10. The boys give Austin a ball signed by Dusty.

---

**Extension:** Have students work in pairs. Ask each student to write two sentences that tell what happens in a baseball game. Then tell students to draw a line under the predicates in their partner's sentences.

# Finding Predicates

> • Every sentence has two parts.
>
> • Every sentence has a predicate.
>
> • The predicate of a sentence tells what the subject does or is.

Match each group of words in the first column with its predicate in the second column. Write the predicate.

1. A toy store _____.

2. The boys _____.

3. A long line of people _____.

4. At first, Max _____.

5. Many people _____.

6. Dusty Field _____.

7. A real league ball _____.

8. Austin _____.

9. Austin's fish _____.

10. From his bag, Gordy _____.

| |
|---|
| is in front of the store |
| spend five dollars |
| is tall and thin |
| has a sale |
| takes out Austin's ball |
| is happy to see his friends |
| buy balls from the boys |
| is nervous |
| costs three dollars |
| eats shrimp |

Extension: Have students complete the following sentence by using different predicates: Once a friend _____.

Book 3.1/Unit 1
**Max Malone Makes a Million**

10

Name_____ Date_____

# Writing Predicates to Complete Sentences

---

> • Every sentence has two parts.
>
> • Every sentence has a predicate.
>
> • The predicate of a sentence tells what the subject does or is.

Add a predicate to each group of words. Write the sentence.

**1.** A baseball pitcher _____.

_____

**2.** A catcher _____.

_____

**3.** On his face, the catcher _____.

_____

**4.** A batter _____.

_____

**5.** After three strikes, a batter _____.

_____

**6.** After a hit, the batter _____.

_____

**7.** Players on the field _____.

_____

**8.** The highest score _____.

_____

---

**Extension:** Ask each student to write on a strip of oak tag a sentence about another sport. Have students cut their sentence into two parts so the predicate is one part. Then display the subjects of students' sentences and invite students to find and match the missing predicates.

# Using Quotation Marks in Sentences

> • Use **quotation marks** before and after a person's exact words.

Put the quotation marks where they should be. Write the correct sentences on the lines.

**1.** That's it! Max cried out.

_____

**2.** You're a genius, said Gordy.

_____

**3.** How many can we buy? asked Gordy.

_____

**4.** Let's ask the manager, said Max.

_____

Proofread these sentences. Write them correctly on the lines.

**5.** max said that's a great idea

_____

**6.** the boys sold the baseballs

_____

**7.** wow said Gordy

_____

**8.** explain how the boys made a million

_____

**Extension:** Have students write a conversation using quotation marks.

# Predicates

**A.** Decide which part of the sentence is the predicate. Mark your answer.

1. A young woman in the store helped the boys.
   - ⓐ helped the boys
   - ⓑ A young woman
   - ⓒ in the store

2. The box of baseballs cost five dollars.
   - ⓐ The box
   - ⓑ cost five dollars
   - ⓒ The box of baseballs

3. Some of the kids had scraps of paper.
   - ⓐ scraps of paper
   - ⓑ had scraps of paper
   - ⓒ Some of the kids

4. Max and Gordy sold all the baseballs.
   - ⓐ Max and Gordy
   - ⓑ sold all the baseballs
   - ⓒ all the baseballs

**B.** Decide which predicate fits the sentence. Mark your answer.

5. The manager of the store _____.
   - ⓐ door opens
   - ⓑ opening the door.
   - ⓒ opened the door.

6. The baseball player _____.
   - ⓐ wore jeans
   - ⓑ wearing jeans
   - ⓒ worn jeans

7. The ball that Dusty signed _____.
   - ⓐ for Austin
   - ⓑ is for Austin
   - ⓒ gave to Austin

8. A real baseball _____.
   - ⓐ be three dollars
   - ⓑ three dollars cost
   - ⓒ costs three dollars

## Predicates

> • The **predicate** of a sentence tells what the subject does or is.

**Mechanics:**
- Begin every sentence with a capital letter.
- End every sentence with a special mark.
- Use quotation marks before and after a person's exact words.

Work with a partner. One of you reads the sentences aloud. The other proofreads. Listen for the sentences that are missing a predicate. Write the corrected sentences on the lines. The proofreader reads the corrected sentences aloud.

I. the Giant Summer Sale

_____

2. max read the sign on a box

_____

3. the perfect things to buy

_____

4. do you know what he bought

_____

5. the baseballs in the box

_____

6. at first, only a few kids

_____

7. they sold all the baseballs

_____

8. tell me how the story ends

_____

# Sentence Combining

> • Two related sentences can be joined with a comma and the word *and*.
> Separate: A baseball is sewn by hand. It has 108 stitches.
> Joined: A baseball is sewn by hand, and it has 108 stitches.

Combine each pair of sentences. Use a comma and the word *and*.

**1.** The pitcher throws the ball. Cardone swings.

_____

_____

**2.** Cardone hits the ball. The ball goes flying.

_____

_____

**3.** Cardone hits a home run. The team pulls ahead.

_____

_____

**4.** The Toms River team wins the World Series. The fans go wild.

_____

_____

**5.** The team rides in a parade. The players wave to their fans.

_____

_____

5   Book 3.1/Unit 1
**Champions of the World**

**Extension:** Have students write two related
sentences of their own about the Toms River team
and then use the word *and* to join them.

25

# Compound Sentences

> • A sentence that contains two sentences joined by *and* is called a
> **compound sentence**.

Write a compound sentence by joining each pair of sentences. Use a
comma and the word *and*.

**1.** Chris Cardone bats for the first time. He hits a home run.

_____

_____

**2.** Todd Frazier is the star pitcher. He also hits a home run.

_____

_____

**3.** Brad Frank tags the player. The player is out.

_____

_____

**4.** A U.S. team wins the World Series. It's the first time since 1993.

_____

_____

**5.** Toms River has a parade. About 2,000 fans come out to cheer.

_____

_____

**26**

**Extension:** Ask students to write a compound sentence
about parades, using the word *and*.

Book 3.1/Unit 1
**Champions of the World**

5

# Writing Compound Sentences

- Two related sentences can be joined with a comma and the word *and*.
- A sentence that contains two sentences joined by *and* is called a **compound sentence**.

Copy the following story, but make it sound better. Use *and* to join each pair of underlined sentences. Place a comma before *and* when you join the sentences to make them into compound sentences.

The baseball game is on. Denise is about to bat. She's all set. The ball zooms toward her. She swings hard. What a hit! Denise takes off for first base. She touches first base. The coach waves her on to second. Denise slides happily into second base.

_____

_____

_____

_____

_____

_____

_____

_____

**Extension:** Have pairs of students proofread each other's stories. Ask students to look for a comma and the word *and* in each compound sentence.

# Proofreading Compound Sentences

> - Use a comma before *and* when you join two sentences to form a compound sentence.
> - Begin every sentence with a capital letter.

Combine each pair of short sentences into one longer sentence. Place a comma in the correct place and begin the second part of the sentence with a small letter. Then rewrite the paragraph.

    One brother plays for the Cubs. The other brother plays for the Tigers. One is a pitcher. The other is a shortstop. Today the brothers are playing in the park. They take turns batting balls. The day is warm. The sunshine feels good. The boys enjoy their practice. Then they go home.

_____

_____

_____

_____

_____

_____

_____

**Extension:** Invite students to write a short story about their favorite sport. Tell students to include two compound sentences in their story.

# Sentence Combining

**A.** Write **yes** if two sentences have been combined. Write **no** if two sentences have not been combined.

I. One team scored 12 points, and the other team scored 9 points.

_____

2. The Toms River team wins the game and the championship.

_____

3. Cardone hits the ball, and the ball is gone.

_____

4. Todd Frazier hits a home run, and he saves the ball.

_____

**B.** If the sentence is a compound sentence, write **compound**. If it is not a compound sentence, write **no**.

5. Sammy Sosa and Mark McGwire set records. _____

6. Sosa hit 66 home runs, and McGwire hit 70. _____

**C.** Use *and* to combine each pair of sentences. Write the new sentence on the line.

7. The batter hit the ball. It sailed over the fence.

_____

8. He hit a home run. His team won the game.

_____

## Sentence Combining

> - A sentence that contains two sentences joined by *and* is called a compound sentence.
> - Use a comma before *and* when you join two sentences to form a compound sentence.
> - Every sentence begins with a capital letter.
> - Every sentence ends with a special mark.

Read the paragraph about the picture. First write the underlined sentences as a compound sentence. Use a comma and the word *and*. Then write the other three sentences correctly on the lines.

the team won the championship. the players were proud. they carried the Little League Championship banner the banner had the year 1999 on it they want to win again

_____

_____

_____

_____

# Sentences

Read the passage and look at the underlined section. Is there a mistake? What type of mistake is it? Mark your answer.

---

My grandfather was born in Japan. <u>he crossed the ocean to come to America.</u> There he saw huge cities. <u>He liked San Francisco best</u>   He decided to live there.
<sub>(1)</sub> ... <sub>(2)</sub>

---

1. ⓐ Capitalization
   ⓑ Punctuation
   ⓒ Spelling
   ⓓ No Mistake

2. ⓔ Capitalization
   ⓕ Punctuation
   ⓖ Spelling
   ⓗ No Mistake

---

I like spelling words about animals. In class, teacher says, "Spell hippopotamus." On no, the word is too long! <u>What do I do now,</u> I remember Hip, Pop, Tam, and us. <u>I got it rght!</u>
<sub>(3)</sub> ... <sub>(4)</sub>

---

3. ⓐ Capitalization
   ⓑ Punctuation
   ⓒ Spelling
   ⓓ No Mistake

4. ⓔ Capitalization
   ⓕ Punctuation
   ⓖ Spelling
   ⓗ No Mistake

---

<u>Visit the land of Opt.</u> There you will meet a king who looks taller than the queen. <u>look again.</u> You will see that the queen seems taller.
<sub>(5)</sub> ... <sub>(6)</sub>

---

5. ⓐ Capitalization
   ⓑ Punctuation
   ⓒ Spelling
   ⓓ No Mistake

6. ⓔ Capitalization
   ⓕ Punctuation
   ⓖ Spelling
   ⓗ No Mistake

---

Read the passage and look at the underlined section. Is there a mistake? If there is, how do you correct it? Mark your answer.

---

I saw balloons float in the air. <u>Were many sizes and colors.</u> They had various shapes. <u>Some balloons.</u> I thought I was dreaming.
                                  (7)
                 (8)

---

**7.** ⓐ Add a subject.
 ⓑ Add a predicate.
 ⓒ Join two sentences with *and.*
 ⓓ No mistake.

**8.** ⓔ Add a subject.
 ⓕ Add a predicate.
 ⓖ Join two sentences with *and.*
 ⓗ No mistake.

---

<u>The beach.</u> Many people go to the beach during summer. I love the beach. <u>I come here to swim. I come here to build sand castles.</u>
   (9)
                                                      (10)

---

**9.** ⓐ Add a subject.
 ⓑ Add a predicate.
 ⓒ Join two sentences with *and.*
 ⓓ No mistake.

**10.** ⓔ Add a subject.
 ⓕ Add a predicate.
 ⓖ Join two sentences with *and.*
 ⓗ No mistake.

# Common and Proper Nouns

- A **noun** names a person, place, or thing.
- A **common noun** names any person, place, or thing.
- A **proper noun** names a special person, place, or thing.
- A proper noun begins with a capital letter.

Write **common** or **proper** under each underlined noun.

1. <u>Marcy</u> and <u>Miss Rosa</u> are <u>neighbors</u>.

   _____

2. <u>Old Man Hammer</u> does not sign the <u>petition</u>.

   _____

3. A <u>woman</u> in the <u>city</u> checks her <u>files</u>.

   _____

4. <u>Mr. Bennett</u> brings <u>wood</u> and <u>tools</u>.

   _____

5. <u>Mr. Rocco</u> brings <u>cans</u> of <u>paint</u>.

   _____

6. <u>Old Man Hammer</u> plants some <u>seeds</u>.

   _____

7. <u>Flowers</u> and <u>vegetables</u> begin to grow.

   _____

8. Soon the <u>lot</u> becomes a <u>garden</u>.

   _____

8 Book 3.1/Unit 2
**City Green**

**Extension:** Ask students to write three proper nouns that name their neighbors and three common nouns that name vegetables.

33

# Proper Nouns: Days, Months, Holidays

> • The name of a day, month, or holiday begins with a capital letter.

Complete the sentences by writing the name of the day, month, or holiday correctly.

**1.** Marcy gets up early on _____.        saturday

**2.** On _____, the city drops off tools.        sunday

**3.** A good time to plant seeds is _____.        april

**4.** Many flowers bloom in _____.        may

**5.** The garden is filled with plants by _____.        july

**6.** Pumpkins grow in _____.        october

**7.** People like pumpkins for _____.        halloween

**8.** I like pumpkin pie for _____.        thanksgiving

**Extension:** Invite students to make up riddles about days, months, and holidays. Have students take turns writing the answers on the board.

# Common and Proper Nouns in Sentences

- A **noun** names a person, place, or thing.
- A **common noun** names any person, place, or thing.
- A **proper noun** names a special person, place, or thing.
- A proper noun begins with a capital letter.

Underline the common nouns and circle the proper nouns. Then use the correct noun from the box to complete each sentence.

| | | | |
|---|---|---|---|
| Leslie | curb | sunflowers | Saturday |
| June | spoon | Miss Rosa | milk |

1. People work in the lot on _____.

2. Marcy's brother carries bags of junk to the _____.

3. When _____ comes to the lot, she brings her baby.

4. The baby digs dirt with a _____.

5. At lunchtime, _____ brings food.

6. She also brings _____ to drink.

7. Summer begins in _____.

8. Old Man Hammer's _____ bloom then.

8  Book 3.1/Unit 2
**City Green**

**Extension:** Have students work with a partner to list a common noun and a proper noun in each category: person, place, and thing.

35

# Abbreviation of Proper Nouns

---

- An abbreviation is a shortened form of a word.
- An abbreviation begins with a capital letter and ends with a period.
- Abbreviate titles of people before names.
  Mrs.   Ms.   Mr.   Dr.
- You can abbreviate days of the week.
- You can also abbreviate most months.

---

Proofread the sentences. Write each abbreviation correctly.

1. Mama's friend mrs B helps clean the lot._____

2. From two houses down, mr Rocco comes._____

3. One day, mrs Wells talks about her grandmother._____

4. mr Bennett doesn't know about the sunflowers._____

5. On mon, Old Man Hammer sits in the garden._____

6. He also comes on tues and every other day._____

7. In aug, Marcy sees him sitting in the sun._____

8. In jan, he probably won't come._____

# Common and Proper Nouns

**A.** If the underlined noun is a common noun, write **common**. If the underlined noun is a proper noun, write **proper**.

1. The <u>building</u> was unsafe. _____

2. <u>Old Man Hammer</u> used to live in it. _____

3. A crane parked on the <u>street.</u> _____

4. <u>Workers</u> knocked down the building. _____

5. <u>Miss Rosa</u> took dirt from the lot. _____

**B.** Find the abbreviation of a proper noun in each sentence. Write it on the line.

6. One of the neighbors was Mr. Rocco. _____

7. Mrs. Wells was another neighbor. _____

8. Apr. is a good month for gardens. _____

9. Dec. is not a good month for gardens. _____

10. Mr. Bennett is a neighbor also. _____

# Common and Proper Nouns

---

- A **noun** names a person, place, or thing.
- A **common noun** names any person, place, or thing.
- A **proper noun** names a special person, place, or thing.

**Mechanics:**

- Begin a proper noun with a capital letter.
- Begin the name of a day, month, or holiday with a capital letter.

Write each sentence correctly. Then use the sentences to draw a picture.

**1.** marcy went to the lot on saturday.

_____

**2.** mr rocco brought paint.

_____

**3.** leslie brought her baby.

_____

**4.** miss rosa brought bread and jelly.

_____

# Singular and Plural Nouns

---

A **singular noun** names one person, place, or thing.

A **plural noun** names more than one person, place, or thing.

Add *-s* to form the plural of most singular nouns.

---

Write the plural form of each noun.

1. year _____
2. twig _____
3. tree _____
4. pebble _____
5. eye _____

6. animal _____
7. valley _____
8. canyon _____
9. grain _____
10. bucket _____

Write the plural form of the noun in parentheses to complete each sentence.

11. The story is about two (mountain) _____.

12. Small (stream) _____ become a raging river.

13. The river grinds rough (rock) _____.

14. Heavy (layer) _____ of sand sink down into the earth.

15. Elizabeth sees sand spread into small (fan) _____.

**15** Book 3.1/Unit 2
**The Sun, the Wind and the Rain**

**Extension:** Have students write four sentences using each of the following words in plural form: million, minute, hand, peak.

**39**

# Forming Plural Nouns

> • Add *-es* to form the plural of singular nouns that end in *s*, *sh*, *ch*, or *x*.
>
> • To form the plural of nouns ending in a consonant and *y*, change the *y* to *i* and add *-es.*

Change each word to a plural noun.

1. story _____
2. beach _____
3. pass _____
4. crack _____
5. wish _____

6. day _____
7. sky _____
8. path _____
9. box _____
10. bunch _____

Write the plural form of each noun in parentheses.

11. My family takes (journey) _____ to the mountains.

12. I look for birds in the (branch) _____ of trees.

13. I also look for birds in (bush) _____.

14. I see birds eating (berry) _____.

15. Sometimes at night we see (fox) _____.

**Extension:** Have students take turns writing singular nouns that end in s, x, ch, sh, and y. Have other students write the plurals of these words.

40

Book 3.1/Unit 2
**The Sun, the Wind and the Rain** 15

# Using Plural Nouns in Sentences

---

> • Add -s to form the plural of most singular nouns.
>
> • Add -es to form the plural of singular nouns that end in s, sh, ch, or x.
>
> • To form the plural of nouns ending in a consonant and y, change the y to i and add -es.

Complete each sentence with the correct singular or plural noun in parentheses.

1. Two (family, families) _____ went to the beach.

2. The parking lot was full of (car, cars) _____.

3. Many (bus, buses) _____ stopped at the beach.

4. The children swam in the (ocean, oceans) _____.

5. One child made a sand (mountain, mountains) _____.

6. Some children picked up (shell, shells) _____.

7. They put them in a small (box, boxes) _____.

8. Someone found a big white (feather, feathers) _____.

9. Everyone ate (sandwich, sandwiches) _____.

10. Then they ate juicy (peach, peaches) _____.

---

**Extension:** Invite students to draw a picture that shows the families at the beach. Then have students use singular and plural nouns to label people, places, and things in their pictures.

# Using Commas

---

- Use commas to separate three or more words in a series.
  There are twigs, pebbles, and shells on the beach.

---

Proofread the sentences. Add commas where they belong.

1. Elizabeth put sand water and rocks in her bucket.

2. She made a mountain out of twigs pebbles and sand.

3. The mountain has animals trees and grass.

4. Animals walked in the lush green and deep valleys.

5. Sun wind and rain can destroy a mountain.

6. The breeze blew sand in Elizabeth's eyes ears and hair.

7. The rain carved valleys hills and lakes into the mountain.

8. The thick heavy and sandy rocks sank into the earth.

9. The earth moved cracked and shifted again.

10. Elizabeth walked home with her hat shovel and bucket.

---

**Extension:** Ask students to write a sentence with three or more words in a series and to use commas where needed.

42

Book 3.1/Unit 2
**The Sun, the Wind and the Rain**

10

# Singular and Plural Nouns

**A.** Read the nouns. Find the noun that is singular. Mark your answer.

1.
- ⓐ rocks
- ⓑ trees
- ⓒ pool
- ⓓ pebbles

2.
- ⓐ breezes
- ⓑ twig
- ⓒ grains
- ⓓ mountains

3.
- ⓐ pass
- ⓑ canyons
- ⓒ layers
- ⓓ cracks

4.
- ⓐ steps
- ⓑ cars
- ⓒ bus
- ⓓ eons

**B.** Read each sentence. Find the correct plural form for the noun in parentheses.

5. The (peak) were sharp.
- ⓐ peakes
- ⓑ peakies
- ⓒ peaks
- ⓓ peak

6. The (beach) were sandy.
- ⓐ beachs
- ⓑ beaches
- ⓒ beach
- ⓓ beachies

7. The (sky) were blue.
- ⓐ skies
- ⓑ skys
- ⓒ skis
- ⓓ skyes

8. The (pebble) were wet.
- ⓐ pebbles
- ⓑ pebblees
- ⓒ pebblies
- ⓓ pebble

# Singular and Plural Nouns

- Add -*s* to form the plural of most singular nouns.

- Add -*es* to form the plural of singular nouns that end in *s*, *sh*, *ch*, or *x*.

- To form the plural of nouns ending in a consonant and *y*, change the *y* to *i* and add -*es*.

**Mechanics:**

- Use commas to separate three or more words in a series.

Listen as your partner reads each sentence aloud. Rewrite the sentences. Correct the underlined nouns. Put commas where they belong.

**1.** I saw many <u>gull crab</u> and <u>snail</u> at the beach.

_____

**2.** My friend picked up a lot of <u>shell stone</u> and <u>stick</u>.

_____

**3.** He had three <u>box</u> full of sand rocks and seaweed.

_____

**4.** I have visited <u>beach</u> in Maine California and Florida.

_____

**5.** Some <u>bush</u> at a beach have <u>berry flower</u> and <u>thorn</u>.

_____

Read the new sentences to your partner. Do they make sense?

# Irregular Plural Nouns

| • Some nouns have special plural forms. |

Draw a line from each noun to its plural form.

1. wolf _____          men

2. life _____          lives

3. man _____          women

4. woman _____          wolves

5. child _____          mice

6. foot _____          children

7. tooth _____          feet

8. mouse _____          calves

9. goose _____          teeth

10. calf _____          geese

10 Book 3.1/Unit 2
**Dream Wolf**

**Extension:** Have the class use the plurals on this page to tell a progressive story. Encourage each student to add a sentence to the story.

45

# More Irregular Plural Nouns

---

- A few nouns are the same in both singular and plural forms.

| **Singular** | **Plural** | **Singular** | **Plural** |
|---|---|---|---|
| sheep | sheep | fish | fish |
| deer | deer | trout | trout |
| buffalo | buffalo | salmon | salmon |
| moose | moose | scissors | scissors |

---

Complete each sentence with the correct plural form of the noun in parentheses.

**1.** The children saw bighorn (sheep) _____ in the hills.

**2.** I have seen (deer) _____ in a forest.

**3.** The Wolf People followed a herd of (buffalo) _____.

**4.** I once saw two (moose) _____.

**5.** Some forests have streams with (fish) _____.

**6.** Rainbow (trout) _____ live in streams.

**7.** I drew a picture of (salmon) _____ jumping in a stream.

**8.** When I find (scissors) _____, I will cut it out.

---

**Extension:** Have pairs of students pantomime the animals on this page. Invite classmates to guess the animals, using the correct plural forms.

# Using Irregular Plural Nouns in Sentences

> • Some nouns have special plural forms.
>
> • A few nouns have the same singular and plural forms.

Rewrite the sentences. Change the underlined word to a plural noun.

**1.** The <u>child</u> left the berry-pickers.

_____

**2.** The <u>woman</u> made little cakes.

_____

**3.** Bighorn <u>sheep</u> lived among the rocks.

_____

**4.** These animals have <u>foot</u> made for climbing.

_____

**5.** They can run faster than <u>deer</u>.

_____

**6.** The smiling wolf showed his <u>tooth</u>.

_____

**7.** The <u>man</u> jumped on their horses.

_____

**8.** People hope that <u>wolf</u> will return.

_____

8 Book 3.1/Unit 2
**Dream Wolf**

**Extension:** Have students work cooperatively to draw a mural. Explain that the mural should show the sentences they wrote using plural nouns.

47

## Proofreading Sentences

---

> • Every sentence begins with a capital letter.
>
> • A statement ends with a period.
>
> • A command ends with a period.
>
> • An exclamation ends with an exclamation point.
>
> • A question ends with a question mark.

Proofread the paragraph. Rewrite it correctly.

      tiblo and his sister left the other children do you know what happened they got lost how scared they must have been a kind wolf helped them get home tell this story to your family

_____

_____

_____

_____

_____

_____

_____

_____

_____

_____

_____

_____

---

**Extension:** Have students work in pairs. Ask each student to write a statement, command, exclamation, or question without a capital letter or end mark. Then have partners write each other's sentence correctly.

# Irregular Plural Nouns

**A.** Decide if the underlined noun is singular or plural. Write your answer on the line.

1. The <u>children</u> came to a stream. _____

2. <u>Trout</u> live in some streams. _____

3. A <u>trout</u> is a kind of salmon. _____

4. <u>Deer</u> are quiet animals. _____

5. A <u>wolf</u> has sharp teeth. _____

**B.** Write **yes** if the plural form of the underlined noun is correct. Write **no** if it is not correct.

6. Tiblo stayed with the <u>womans</u>. _____

7. He and his sister saw <u>sheep</u>. _____

8. They did not see any <u>mooses</u>. _____

9. The Wolf People heard <u>wolves</u> call. _____

10. The <u>cattle</u> ate the grass. _____

# Irregular Plural Nouns

- Some nouns have special plural forms.
- A few nouns have the same singular and plural forms.

**Mechanics:**
- Every sentence begins with a capital letter.
- A statement ends with a period.
- A command ends with a period.
- An exclamation ends with an exclamation point.
- A question ends with a question mark.

Look at the picture. Find the plural nouns in the paragraph that are wrong. Use the "take out" proofreading mark ( ). Then write the correct forms. Draw three lines under each letter that should be a capital letter. Put in the missing end marks.

A wolf may have gray, brown, red, black, or white fur. a wolf hunts mooses and deers for food Wolfs hunt together in packs. they live in families for a long time Do you know how one wolf talks to another wolf What a great sound a wolf makes write a sentence telling about this sound.

_____

_____

_____

_____

# Singular Possessive Nouns

---

> • A **possessive noun** is a noun that shows who or what owns or has something.
>
> • Add an **apostrophe** (') and an -s to a singular noun to make it possessive.

Write the possessive form of each underlined noun. The first one is done for you.

**1.** the spokes of the <u>web</u>          the web's spokes

**2.** the bite of the <u>spider</u>          the _____ bite

**3.** the shape of the <u>mark</u>          the _____ shape

**4.** the age of the <u>tarantula</u>          the _____ age

**5.** the crops of the <u>farmer</u>          the _____ crops

Read the lists of things that tell about a spider and an ant. Write out each thing as a singular possessive noun. Example: a spider's web.

a spider                         an ant

**6.** thread _____          **11.** feelers _____

**7.** food _____          **12.** body _____

**8.** mate _____          **13.** legs _____

**9.** eyes _____          **14.** color _____

**10.** speed _____          **15.** size _____

---

**14** Book 3.1/Unit 2
**Spiders at Work**

**Extension:** Have students use three of the possessive nouns on this page in oral sentences.

51

# Plural Possessive Nouns

- Add an apostrophe (') to make most plural nouns possessive.
  Example: spiders' webs

- Add an apostrophe (') and an *s* to form the possessive of plural nouns that do not end in *s*.
  Example: men's strength

Write the possessive form of each underlined noun.

1. the victims of the <u>spiders</u>  the _____ victims

2. the threads of the <u>webs</u>  the _____ threads

3. the hairs of the <u>tarantulas</u>  the _____ hairs

4. the pets of some <u>children</u>  some _____ pets

5. the builders of <u>nature</u>  _____ builders

6. the patterns of the <u>blankets</u>  the _____ patterns

7. the skills of the <u>people</u>  the _____ skills

8. the feelers of an <u>insect</u>  an _____ feelers

9. the bodies of the <u>insects</u>  the _____ bodies

10. the legs of the <u>arachnid</u>  the _____ legs

**Extension:** Have each student use the possessive form of a noun in a sentence.

Book 3.1/Unit 2
**Spiders at Work** 10

# Possessive Nouns in Sentences

---

- A **possessive noun** is a noun that shows who or what owns or has something.

- Add an **apostrophe** (') and an *s* to a singular noun to make it possessive.

- Add an apostrophe (') to make most plural nouns possessive.

- Add an apostrophe (') and an *s* to form the possessive of plural nouns that do not end in *s*.

---

Complete each sentence with the possessive form of the noun in parentheses.

**1.** It was both (classes) _____ idea to walk in the woods.

**2.** We looked for (spiders) _____ webs.

**3.** We saw a (spider) _____ bridge line.

**4.** We also saw lots of (deer) _____ hoofprints.

**5.** The (trees) _____ seeds were scattered on the ground.

**6.** The (bushes) _____ berries were red.

**7.** On our walk, we found five kinds of (birds) _____ nests.

**8.** We heard a (bluebird) _____ song.

**9.** Some children found a (hawk) _____ feathers.

**10.** The teachers answered the (children) _____ questions.

[10] Book 3.1/Unit 2
**Spiders at Work**

**Extension:** Have students find examples of ads that include plural possessive nouns.

53

# Correcting Possessive Nouns

---

- Add an apostrophe (') and an *s* to a singular noun to make it possessive.

- Add an apostrophe (') to make most plural nouns possessive.

- Add an apostrophe (') and an *s* to form the possessive of plural nouns that do not end in *s*.

---

Rewrite each sentence. Use the correct possessive form of the underlined word.

1. Water <u>spiders</u> homes are underwater.

   _____

2. A garden <u>spider</u> web is strong.

   _____

3. Some spiders are as small as a <u>pin</u> head.

   _____

4. Black widows can cause <u>humans</u> death.

   _____

5. A black <u>widow</u> bite is poisonous.

   _____

6. <u>Rattlesnakes</u> venom is not as deadly.

   _____

7. In Africa, some <u>children</u> stories are about a spider.

   _____

8. The <u>story</u> main character is called Anansi.

   _____

---

**Extension:** Have students use the possessive nouns *spider's, spiders', bush's, bushes'* in sentences of their own and draw pictures to illustrate each sentence.

# Possessive Nouns

**A.** Read each sentence. Find the correct possessive form for the singular noun in parentheses.

1. A (spider) web looks like a wheel.
   - ⓐ spiders
   - ⓑ spider's
   - ⓒ spiders'
   - ⓓ spiders's

2. The (web) spokes are dry.
   - ⓐ webs
   - ⓑ web
   - ⓒ web's
   - ⓓ webs'

**B.** Read each sentence. Find the correct possessive form for the plural noun in parentheses.

3. Water (spiders) webs are balloon-shaped.
   - ⓐ spiders'
   - ⓑ spider's
   - ⓒ spider'
   - ⓓ spiders's

4. (Flies) bodies have two parts.
   - ⓐ Flie's
   - ⓑ Flys'
   - ⓒ Fly's
   - ⓓ Flies'

5. Some (people) pets are tarantulas.
   - ⓐ peoples'
   - ⓑ people'
   - ⓒ people's
   - ⓓ peoples

# Possessive Nouns

> • A **possessive noun** is a noun that shows who or what owns or has something.

**Mechanics:**

• Add an apostrophe (') and an *s* to a singular noun to make it possessive.

• Add an apostrophe (') to make most plural nouns possessive.

• Add an apostrophe (') and an *s* to form the possessive of plural nouns that do not end in *s*.

Work with a partner. One of you reads the sentences aloud. The other proofreads. Look for the possessive forms of singular nouns and plural nouns. Put in the missing apostrophes. The proofreader reads the corrected sentences aloud.

**1.** The spider is natures spinner.

**2.** All spider webs threads are strong.

**3.** A bridge lines thread is silk.

**4.** The black widows bite is poisonous.

**5.** Tarantulas bodies are hairy.

# Sentence Combining with Nouns

> • Two sentences can be combined by joining two nouns with *and*.
> Separate:    "Web Wonders" tells about spiders.
>                     "Web Wonders" tells about scientists.
> Combined:  "Web Wonders" tells about spiders and scientists.

Combine the sentences. Use *and* to join the two underlined nouns.
Write the new sentence.

**1.** Spiders may live in <u>holes</u>. Spiders may live in <u>water</u>.

_____

**2.** A spider's web can trap <u>insects</u>. A spider's web can trap <u>birds</u>.

_____

**3.** Tarantulas have <u>eight legs</u>. Tarantulas have <u>eight eyes</u>.

_____

**4.** Tarantulas eat <u>beetles</u>. Tarantulas eat <u>caterpillars</u>.

_____

**5.** Strong spider silk may stop <u>arrows</u>. Strong spider silk may stop <u>jet planes</u>.

_____

_____

**Extension:** Have students copy this story starter two times: I would use spider silk to make _____. Ask students to complete each sentence with a noun and then combine the sentences by joining the nouns with *and*. **57**

# Combining Subjects

---

> • Some nouns are the subjects of sentences. Sometimes two subjects can be joined with *and*.
>
> Separate:   Adult spiders travel on threads in the wind.
>
> Spiderlings travel on threads in the wind.
>
> Combined: Adult spiders and spiderlings travel on threads in the wind.

Combine the subjects of the sentences. Write the new sentence.

**1.** Flies are meals for spiders. Dragonflies are meals for spiders.

_____

**2.** Tarantulas eat grasshoppers. Daddy-longlegs eat grasshoppers.

_____

**3.** Bird spider tarantulas eat birds. Golden silk spiders eat birds.

_____

**4.** Farmers like spiders. Scientists like spiders.

_____

**5.** Spiders are making spider silk. Scientists are making spider silk.

_____

---

**Extension:** Arrange students in pairs. Have partners take turns generating and extending sentences. One partner thinks of a sentence with one noun in the subject. The other student extends the sentence by adding *and* and another noun.

Book 3.1/Unit 2
**Web Wonders**

5

# Combining Subjects and Objects

---

- Two sentences can be combined by joining two nouns with *and*.
  Separate:     "Web Wonders" tells about spiders.
                       "Web Wonders" tells about scientists.
  Combined:    "Web Wonders" tells about spiders and scientists.

- Some nouns are the objects of sentences. Sometimes two objects can be joined with *and*.

---

Join each pair of sentences. Use *and* to join the nouns. Write the new sentence.

**1.** Elena read about spiders. Elena read about butterflies.

_____

**2.** She learned about spider silk. She learned about human-made silk.

_____

**3.** Pang looked for spider webs. Elena looked for spider webs.

_____

**4.** Garden spiders spin webs. Golden silk spiders spin webs.

_____

**5.** Pang drew pictures of webs. Pang drew pictures of spiders.

_____

**6.** He drew a tarantula. He drew a black widow spider.

_____

**7.** Tarantulas live in holes. Wolf spiders live in holes.

_____

**8.** Spiders are living things. Plants are living things.

_____

---

**Extension:** Have students write a pair of sentences with similar ideas and then join the sentences by combining the nouns.

# Using Commas and Capital Letters in a Letter

- Begin the greeting and closing in a letter with a capital letter.
- Use a comma after the greeting in a letter.
- Use a comma after the closing in a letter.

Proofread this letter. Correct the capitalization and punctuation mistakes. Combine the underlined sentences. Rewrite the letter correctly on the lines.

dear uncle jack

we learned a lot about spiders today do you know how amazing spider webs are <u>spider webs can trap birds. spider webs can trap flies</u>

your niece
jan

(Greeting)

_____

_____

_____

_____

_____

(Closing)

_____

(Your name)

_____

60

**Extension:** Have students proofread their letters and use proofreading marks to show corrections. Then have students rewrite their letters correctly.

Book 3.1/Unit 2
**Web Wonders** 14

# Sentence Combining with Nouns

**A.** Write **yes** if the sentences can be combined by joining two nouns. Write **no** if they cannot be combined.

I. Webs catch flies. Webs catch bees. _____

2. Spiders spin circles. Spiders spin triangles. _____

3. Spiderlings are baby spiders. Spiderlings spin a silk line._____

4. Spider silk may be in jeans. Spider silk may be in coats. _____

**B.** Each pair of sentences can be combined. Write the two nouns that can be joined with the word *and*. Use capital letters correctly.

5. Flies have six legs. Ants have six legs.

_____ and _____

6. Ants do not spin webs. Tarantulas do not spin webs.

_____ and _____

7. Ants have feelers. Beetles have feelers.

_____ and _____

8. Tarantulas have no feelers. Daddy-longlegs have no feelers.

_____ and _____

# Sentence Combining with Nouns

---

- Two sentences can be combined by joining two nouns with *and*.
- Some nouns are the subjects of sentences.
- Sometimes two subjects can be joined with *and*.

Read the sentences about the picture. Combine the sentences by joining the underlined nouns with *and*.

1. Spiders attach webs to <u>plants</u>.
   Spiders attach webs to <u>walls</u>.

   _____

2. Some spiders live in <u>trees</u>.
   Some spiders live in <u>basements</u>.

   _____

3. <u>Grass spiders</u> spin webs in plants.
   <u>Triangle spiders</u> spin webs in plants.

   _____

4. <u>Jumping spiders</u> are colorful.
   <u>Crab spiders</u> are colorful.

   _____

# Nouns

Read each passage. Choose a word or group of words that belong in each space. Mark your answer.

My sister went on a trip to the Arizona desert. She saw beautiful patterns on the __(1)__. She saw colorful rocks. The sun changed from yellow to orange. The sky turned from blue to pink. She told me, "The __(2)__ is like a painting."

1.  (a) fine
    (b) sand
    (c) blow
    (d) brown

2.  (e) desert
    (f) see
    (g) hot
    (h) dry

Dad goes to work at Wooly's Store in __(3)__. He went yesterday. Today __(4)__ is home. There was an accident at the store. A toy display caught fire. People were scared. They forgot to call the Newtown Fire Department.

3.  (a) Newtown
    (b) country
    (c) ride
    (d) morning

4.  (e) scare
    (f) tall
    (g) men
    (h) Dad

From my window I watch the doves fly above the rooftops. The __(5)__ wings flap as they soar up the sky. They can swoop down to the ground. Sometimes, they look like __(6)__.

5.  (a) doves
    (b) dove's
    (c) doves'
    (d) dove

6.  (e) airplanes
    (f) airplane's
    (g) airplane
    (h) airplanes'

Grandfather flew home to Canada. We brought him to the airport. There were many men, __(7)__, and children waiting for the plane. The __(8)__ bags were lost. Grandfather helped to find them.

**7.** ⓐ woman's
ⓑ womans
ⓒ women
ⓓ women's

**8.** ⓔ children
ⓕ children's
ⓖ childrens'
ⓗ childrens

Last night, the snow fell and covered our yard. My brother and I ran outside. We threw snowballs at each other __(9)__ made a snowman. I forgot my cap __(10)__. I was freezing!

**9.** ⓐ do
ⓑ snow
ⓒ white
ⓓ and

**10.** ⓔ and my mittens
ⓕ my mittens
ⓖ mittens
ⓗ cap's mittens

Spiders can spin circles __(11)__ to make webs. Some spiders make their webs in trees. Some make their webs in houses. Webs catch __(12)__ and bees.

**11.** ⓐ and triangles
ⓑ triangles
ⓒ and
ⓓ not

**12.** ⓔ fly
ⓕ flies
ⓖ flys
ⓗ flie's

# What Is an Action Verb?

---

• An **action verb** is a word that shows action.

   The students <u>clap</u> to the music.

   Moses <u>beats</u> a drum.

---

Each sentence has an action verb. Find the verb and write it on the line.

**1.** Mr. Samuels's class rides on a bus. _____

**2.** Mr. Samuels carries his bag. _____

**3.** He takes them to a concert. _____

**4.** Moses sits in the front row. _____

**5.** A young woman walks onstage. _____

**6.** The percussionist bows. _____

**7.** Some of the students wave. _____

**8.** The conductor raises his baton. _____

**9.** The percussionist hits the gong. _____

**10.** The students thank Ms. Elwyn. _____

---

**Extension:** Have students work together in pairs. Ask them to list verbs that show the actions of playing instruments. Once they have completed their lists, they can check the story to see if they can find additional musical action verbs.

# Finding Action Verbs

> • An **action verb** is a word that shows action. Some action verbs tell about actions that are hard to see.
> The students <u>listen</u> to the music.
> Moses <u>likes</u> the vibrations.

Circle the action verb in each sentence.

 1. The teacher waits for the class.

 2. The conductor smiles at the audience.

 3. The students watch the conductor carefully.

 4. They enjoy the concert!

 5. Moses feels the vibrations in the balloon.

 6. The students learn the music.

 7. The drums make a lot of noise.

 8. They practice their instruments.

 9. They helped each other.

10. Moses remembers that field trip.

**66**

**Extension:** Have the students work in pairs and list four action verbs. Using their list, they should take turns writing sentences using the verbs.

Book 3.1/Unit 3
**Moses Goes to a Concert**
10

# Using Action Verbs

> • An **action verb** is a word that shows action.
>
> • Some action verbs tell about actions that are hard to see.
>
>   Maria <u>plays</u> the congas.
>
>   Moses <u>counts</u> the beats.

Here is a list of action verbs. Choose an action verb to finish each sentence. Write the verb on the line.

| | |
|---|---|
| bows | meet |
| climbs | strikes |
| likes | watches |
| feel | wonders |

I. Mr. Samuels's class _____ into the bus.

2. The class _____ about the surprise.

3. Moses _____ his drum.

4. The percussionist _____.

5. The members of the orchestra _____ the conductor.

6. The percussionist _____ the gong.

7. The deaf students _____ the vibrations.

8. The class _____ Ms. Elwyn.

8 | Book 3.1/Unit 3
**Moses Goes to a Concert**

**Extension:** Ask students to write three sentences telling about a favorite activity. Tell them to use action verbs in their sentences.

67

# Using Capital Letters and Commas

---

- A proper noun begins with a **capital letter**.
- The name of a day, month, or holiday beings with a **capital letter**.
- Use a **comma** between the name of a city and a state.
- Use a **comma** between the day and the year in a date.

---

Correct each sentence. Write the capital letter over the small letter.
Add commas.

1. mr. samuels teaches deaf students.

2. He was born on march 31 1960.

3. The class went to a concert last wednesday.

4. On the bus, moses sat next to john.

5. The conductor is from boston massachusetts.

6. Many holidays are celebrated on a monday.

7. The percussionist once played in dayton ohio.

8. We watched the parade on november 26 1998.

9. After the concert, diane, mark, and steve played the drums.

10. One school for the deaf opened on september 4 1964.

---

**Extension:** Have the students write three sentences about a recent holiday. Ask them to give the date and day of the week that they celebrated the holiday, along with details of what they did.

**68**

Book 3.1/Unit 3
**Moses Goes to a Concert**

10

# Action Verbs

Read each sentence. Find the action verb and write it on the line.

1. He plays the piano. _____

2. The class dances to the vibrations. _____

3. Ms. Elwyn takes a bow. _____

4. Moses chooses the bass drum. _____

5. She listens to music. _____

Find the action verb in the list that best fits each sentence. Write the verb on the line next to the sentence.

| gives | knows | nods | pounds | shows |
|-------|-------|------|--------|-------|

6. Moses _____ John his new drum. _____

7. Mr. Samuels _____ them balloons. _____

8. The conductor _____ to the soloist. _____

9. She _____ the tom-toms. _____

10. The player _____ the signal. _____

# Action Verbs

> • An **action verb** is a word that shows action.
>
> • Some action verbs tell about actions that are hard to see.
>   Ms. Elwyn <u>taps</u> the cymbals.
>   The concert <u>makes</u> them happy.

Draw a line from each sentence to the picture of the action it tells about. Underline the action verb in each sentence.

**1.** The percussionist shakes the fancy maracas.

**2.** The students wait in the school bus.

**3.** She plucks the strings of the harp.

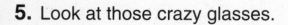

**4.** Moses sits in his stocking feet.

**5.** Look at those crazy glasses.

# Present-Tense Verbs

- A verb in the **present tense** tells what happens now.

- A present-tense verb must **agree** with its subject.

- Add –s to most verbs if the subject is singular.

- Do not add –s to a present-tense verb when the subject is plural or I or you.

Each sentence below is followed by two forms of a verb. Choose the form of the verb that correctly agrees with the subject of the sentence. Circle your answer.

| | | |
|---|---|---|
| 1. Fernando ____ in a tiny village. | live | lives |
| 2. His parents ____ hard. | work | works |
| 3. "I ____ paper for my paintings." | need | needs |
| 4. "You ____ to paint our house?" | want | wants |
| 5. His neighbors ____ what he is doing. | wonder | wonders |
| 6. Fernando's plan ____ good. | look | looks |
| 7. He ____ vines, trees, and animals. | paint | paints |
| 8. Señora Alfaro ____ Fernando to paint her house also. | ask | asks |

8

Book 3.1/Unit 3
**The Little Painter of Sabana Grande**

**Extension:** Have students write about the actions they do every afternoon when they get home from school.

71

# Present-Tense Verbs

- A verb in the **present tense** tells what happens now.

- A present-tense verb must **agree** with its subject.

- Add *–es* to verbs that end in *s, ch, sh, x,* or *z* if the subject is singular.

- Change *y* to *i* and add *–es* to verbs that end with a consonant and *y.*

- Do not add *–es* to a present-tense verb when the subject is plural or *I* or *you.*

  He <u>fishes</u>.    The paint <u>dries</u>.
  They <u>fish</u>.    The dishes <u>dry</u>.

For each verb below, write the form that agrees with the subject given.

**1.** hurry        Fernando _____.

**2.** catch        We _____.

**3.** brush        They _____.

**4.** fix          Señor Espino _____.

**5.** carry        You _____.

**6.** bless        Señora Arias _____.

**7.** wax          The painter _____.

**8.** search       I _____.

**Extension:** Have students write three or four sentences
telling the story of the little painter in the present
tense.

# Present-Tense Verbs

---

- A verb in the **present tense** tells what happens now.
- A present tense verb must **agree** with its subject.
- Add –s to most verbs if the subject is singular.
- Add –es to verbs that end in s, ch, sh, x, or z if the subject is singular.
- Change y to i and add –es to verbs that end with a consonant and y.
- Do not add –s or –es to a present-tense verb when the subject is plural or I or you.

---

Pick the correct singular or plural form of the verb in each sentence below. Underline your answer.

1. The Panama country people (mix, mixes) paint using natural dyes.

2. The water (flow, flows) fast in the brook.

3. Fernando (scratch, scratches) pictures in the dirt.

4. His parents (wish, wishes) he could find paper.

5. Fernando's mama (worry, worries) about his painting the house.

6. The neighbors (gather, gathers) to see him paint.

7. The painted vine (reach, reaches) almost to the roof.

8. "You (paint, paints) very well," his teacher tells him.

9. They (confess, confesses) that they like the result.

10. The villagers (enjoy, enjoys) Fernando's pictures.

---

Book 3.1/Unit 3
**The Little Painter of Sabana Grande**
10

**Extension:** Have students work in pairs to write sentences using singular verbs that end in s, ch, sh, x, z, and a consonant followed by y. The class may need to brainstorm together to come up with at least one verb for each type.

73

# Using Abbreviations

---

- An **abbreviation** is a shortened form of a word.
- An abbreviation begins with a **capital letter** and ends with a **period.**
- Abbreviate most **titles of people** before names.

---

Correct the abbreviation in each sentence. Write the capital letter over the small letter. Add the missing periods.

**1.** I hope to see mr Lester today.

**2.** What did dr Cole tell you?

**3.** Jane saw mrs White at the grocery store.

**4.** Dana moved to Main st last week.

**5.** We waited for ms Vendome to call.

**6.** Let's watch the parade on st Patrick's Day.

**7.** West pt is a famous military school.

**8.** My mom bought a book by prof Daniels.

**9.** We read about gen George Washington today.

**10.** River rd is a busy street.

---

74

**Extension:** Have small groups of students create lists of capitalized abbreviations. Using the individual lists, create a class list for later review.

Book 3.1/Unit 3
**The Little Painter of Sabana Grande**

10

# Present-Tense Verbs

**A.** Choose the correct form for each of the following verbs to go with the singular subject in the sentence below. Mark your answer.

Sentence: Fernando _____.

1. ⓐ guess
   ⓑ guesses
   ⓒ guessies
   ⓓ guessess

2. ⓐ carrys
   ⓑ carryes
   ⓒ carris
   ⓓ carries

3. ⓐ rushes
   ⓑ rush
   ⓒ rushs
   ⓓ rushies

4. ⓐ paintes
   ⓑ paint
   ⓒ paints
   ⓓ paintses

**B.** Decide if the subject of each sentence is singular or plural. Then choose the correct verb to agree with the subject. Mark your answer.

5. Mama ____ Fernando to paint carefully.
   ⓐ tell
   ⓑ tells

6. The neighbors ____ as the painting unfolds.
   ⓐ watch
   ⓑ watches

7. Fernando always ____ his brushes.
   ⓐ wash
   ⓑ washes

8. No one ____ Fernando for his paintings.
   ⓐ pay
   ⓑ pays

## Present-Tense Verbs

---

- A present tense verb must **agree** with its subject.

- Add *–s* or *–es* to verbs if the subject is singular.

- Change *y* to *i* and add *-es* to verbs that end with a consonant and *y*.

- Do not add *–s* or *–es* to a present-tense verb when the subject is plural or *I* or *you*.
  He <u>fishes</u>.        The paint <u>dries</u>.
  I <u>fish</u>.            We <u>dry</u> the dishes.

---

Work with a partner. One of you can read each sentence aloud while the other person writes down and corrects the verb in the sentence. The verbs are underlined.

**1.** Fernando's teacher <u>tell</u> him how to make paints. _____

**2.** It <u>tax</u> his patience to make them. _____

**3.** He <u>try</u> to find paper. _____

**4.** Fernando's fingers <u>itches</u> to paint. _____

**5.** His parents <u>sees</u> his sadness. _____

**6.** He <u>wish</u> to paint on the white adobe house. _____

**7.** Mama and Papa finally <u>agrees</u> to let Fernando paint the house.

_____

**8.** Fernando <u>sketch</u> a tiny plan. _____

**9.** "I <u>likes</u> your plan," Papa says. _____

**10.** The village <u>buzz</u> with excitement. _____

Now the partner who corrected the sentences can read them aloud.

---

# Past-Tense Verbs

- A verb in the **past tense** tells about an action that already happened.

- Add *-ed* to most verbs to show past tense.
  Grandma <u>waited</u> for the scraps.

Find the past-tense verb in each sentence. Write it on the line.

**1.** Tanya wanted to go outside. _____

**2.** She looked longingly out the window._____

**3.** Grandma flexed her fingers. _____

**4.** Tanya remembered some of the fabrics in the scraps. _____

**5.** Mama complained about the mess. _____

**6.** "A year," shouted Tanya. _____

**7.** One by one, Grandma added each person to the quilt. _____

**8.** Tanya and her family romped in the snow. _____

**9.** Grandma grouped the scraps in a pattern of colors. _____

**10.** Mama helped Grandma with the quilt. _____

**Extension:** Have students write present-tense verbs on scraps of paper, and shuffle the scraps for them to pick. Have each student spell the past-tense form of his or her verb and use it in a sentence.

## Past-Tense Verbs

---

- If a verb ends with *e*, drop the *e* and add *–ed* to show past tense.

- If a verb ends with a consonant and *y*, change *y* to *i* and add *–ed*.

- If a verb ends with one vowel and one consonant, double the consonant and add *–ed*.

  pull, **pulled**      carry, **carried**

  arrive, **arrived**    clap, **clapped**

---

Change each underlined verb to past tense. Write the past-tense verb on the line.

**1.** All last year, Grandma <u>trim</u> scraps for the quilt. _____

**2.** That December, Mama <u>cook</u> for Christmas all day. _____

**3.** At that time, Grandma <u>join</u> her in the kitchen. _____

**4.** Last night, she <u>fold</u> the quilt neatly. _____

**5.** A week ago, Mama and Papa <u>permit</u> them to see Grandma.

   _____

**6.** Last night, Grandma <u>smile</u> at Ted, Jim, and Tanya. _____

**7.** That spring, Tanya <u>hurry</u> home each day to work on the quilt.

   _____

**8.** Last week, Tanya <u>stop</u> working on the quilt. _____

**9.** Yesterday, she <u>tiptoe</u> into Grandma's room. _____

**10.** Starting last month, Papa <u>carry</u> Grandma to her chair. _____

---

**Extension:** Have students work in pairs to list ten past-tense verbs that describe the actions of making a quilt. Develop a glossary page, giving their own definition for each verb. Encourage them to illustrate their glossary pages.

Book 3.1/Unit 3
**The Patchwork Quilt**
10

# Past-Tense Verbs

---

- A verb in the **past tense** tells about an action that already happened.
- Add *–ed* to most verbs to show past tense.
- If a verb ends in *e*, drop the *e* and add *–ed* to show past tense.
- If a verb ends with a consonant and *y*, change *y* to *i* and add *–ed*.
- If a verb ends with one vowel and one consonant, double the consonant and add *–ed*.

Choose the correct past-tense verb for each sentence. Circle your answer.

1. Grandma \_\_\_\_\_ together the quilt all year.            pieces        pieced

2. Tanya \_\_\_\_\_ her head.            tilted        tiltted

3. Grandma never \_\_\_\_\_ old material.            scrapped        scraped

4. Often that year, Mama \_\_\_\_\_ about Grandma.            worry        worried

5. Yesterday, Jim \_\_\_\_\_ Grandma.            hugs        hugged

6. All last winter, Mama \_\_\_\_\_ his pants again and again.            patched        patches

7. In her flowing costume, Tanya \_\_\_\_\_.            danceded        danced

8. "Look at the snow!" they \_\_\_\_\_.            cryed        cried

9. Mama \_\_\_\_\_ the fabric between her fingers.            rubbed        rubs

10. That first night, the quilt \_\_\_\_\_ each person of something different.            remind        reminded

---

10  Book 3.1/Unit 3
**The Patchwork Quilt**

**Extension:** Have students write brief paragraphs about a past holiday celebration in their families.

79

# Using Commas

> • Use commas to separate three or more words in a series.
>
>   Mama <u>shopped</u>, <u>cooked</u>, and <u>served</u> dinner.

Correct the sentences by changing the verbs to past-tense. Add a comma after words in a series. Write the new sentence on the line.

**1.** Mama look at Grandma pick up Tanya's glass and went out.

_____

**2.** Grandma turn away gaze out the window and rub the cloth.

_____

**3.** Grandma say, "I need more gold blue green and red material."

_____

**4.** Grandma and Mama hum talk and laugh as they work.

_____

**5.** The two women cut place and sew the scraps.

_____

**6.** The quilt include scraps from Ted Jim Tanya Mama and Papa.

_____

**7.** Tanya work all February March and April on the quilt.

_____

**8.** The finished quilt look big bright and colorful.

_____

**Extension:** Hold a "scavenger hunt" for verbs, nouns, and adjectives in a
series. The first student to find a series of each kind of word wins the hunt.
80   The students can search in magazines, catalogs, and newspapers.

Book 3.1/Unit 3
**The Patchwork Quilt**   8

# Past-Tense Verbs

Read each sentence. Find the past-tense verb and write it on the line.

**I.** Tanya hoped to go outside. _____

**2.** She leaned against Grandma's chair. _____

**3.** Grandma patted Tanya's head. _____

**4.** The students scurried outside to enjoy the snow. _____

Spell the past-tense form of the action verb in each sentence. Write the answer on the line.

**5.** "A whole year!" Tanya (cry) last spring. _____

**6.** Beginning that day, Grandma (plan) her quilt. _____

**7.** Tanya (amaze) her family that year. _____

**8.** All that spring, they (watch) her working on the quilt. _____

**9.** That day, Grandma (pin) some scraps together. _____

**10.** Back then, nobody (imagine) the quilt's final size. _____

## Past Tense Verbs

---

- A verb in the **past tense** tells about an action that already happened.
- Add *–ed* to most verbs to show past tense.
- If a verb ends in *e*, drop the *e* and add *–ed* to show past tense.
- If a verb ends with a consonant and *y*, change *y* to *i* and add *–ed*.
- If a verb ends with one vowel and one consonant, double the consonant and add *–ed*.

---

Look at the picture and read the paragraph that tells what happened. Cross out each verb that is not spelled correctly to show a past action. Write the correct past tense verb above the crossed out verb.

Yesterday, we bakeed a cake together.

Mama explainned the directions.

Grandma measure the flour and sugar.

I stired the batter.

I trys not to spill any!

Now write two or three sentences about how the cake was finished.

_____

_____

_____

---

# Using Verb Tenses

> • A **present-tense verb** tells what happens now.
>   Cookie <u>cooks</u> beans every day.
>
> • A **past-tense verb** tells about an action that already happened.
>   Pecos Bill <u>jumped</u> on the mustang.

Circle the verb in each sentence. Decide whether it is in the present tense or the past tense. Write **present** or **past** on the line.

1. Cowboy Sam orders pizza for dinner. _____

2. Cowgirl Pam and Cowboy Sam tell a story. _____

3. The legend of Pecos Bill started in Texas. _____

4. Pecos Bill's family moved west. _____

5. Bill dropped out of the wagon. _____

6. Ranch Hand #3 wonders about the pizza. _____

7. Pecos Bill joined a family of coyotes. _____

8. Years later, Bill learned human ways from his brother. _____

9. The pizza finally arrives. _____

10. Pecos Bill married Slue-Foot Sue. _____

**Extension:** Have students work in small groups. Ask them to write short skits (five lines at most) using the same characters as those in *Pecos Bill*. They can write in either the present tense or the past tense. Later, they can act out their skits.

# Future Tense

> - A verb in the **future tense** tells about an action that is going to happen.
> - To write about the future, use the special verb *will*.
>   Cookie <u>will cook</u> lima bean pizza.

Find the future tense verb in each sentence. Underline your answer.

1. Pecos Bill will become a legendary cowboy.

2. He will meet his brother, Carl the Cowboy.

3. Carl will teach him in three days.

4. Bill will surprise Carl with his abilities.

5. He will chase Widow Maker across several states.

6. Pecos Bill will invent the lasso.

7. He will make the world's first guitar.

8. In the Rio Grande, he will find his future wife, Slue-Foot Sue.

9. The coyotes will attend the wedding, too.

10. All of them will live happily ever after.

**Extension:** Have each student write about what they think they will be in the future. They can start with " I think that I..." Encourage them to be fanciful if they wish. If time allows, they can illustrate their statements.

Book 3.1/Unit 3
**Pecos Bill**

10

# Using Verb Tenses

---

- A **present-tense verb** tells what happens now.
- A **past-tense verb** tells about an action that already happened.
- A verb in the **future tense** tells about an action that is going to happen.
- To write about the future, use the special verb *will*.

Each sentence below has a time clue that tells if the action is happening now, in the past, or in the future. Choose the correct form of the verb to complete each sentence. Write your answer on the line.

**1.** Now the ranch hands (wait, waited) for dinner. _____

**2.** Tonight, Cowgirl Pam (will tell, tell) a story. _____

**3.** In the early days of ranching, Pecos Bill (uses, used) a lasso.

_____

**4.** Today, Carl the Cowboy (stumbles, stumbled) upon Pecos Bill.

_____

**5.** Years ago, the coyotes (treat, treated) Bill as their own student.

_____

**6.** In the past, Bill (acts, acted) the same as a coyote. _____

**7.** Now he (discovers, discovered) his human nature. _____

**8.** For many years, he (rushes, rushed) around the Southwest.

_____

**9.** Last night, Cowboy Sam (completes, completed) the story.

_____

**10.** Tomorrow, the store (delivered, will deliver) the pizza. _____

---

**Extension:** Ask each student to describe one of the adventures of Pecos Bill using the present tense. They should record their sentences.

# Using Quotation Marks

---

- Use **quotation marks** at the beginning and end of a person's exact words.
  "Come and get it!" Cookie yelled.

- Use a **comma** after the name of a person being spoken to.
  "Cowboy Sam, will you help me?" she asked.

---

Correct each sentence. Add quotation marks at the beginning and end of the person's words. Put a comma after the name of any person being spoken to.

1. Cookie we're tired of eating beans! yelled Cowgirl Pam.

2. Cowgirl Pam will you tell us a story? pleaded Ranch Hand #3.

3. Pa called, Ma we've got new neighbors!

4. I'm Carl the Cowboy. What's your name? asked Carl.

5. Carl insisted, Son you are not a coyote.

6. I'm going to name this horse Widow Maker, Bill shouted.

7. My pa was named Pa too, Bill said.

8. The pizza is here! Yes! said Ranch Hand #3.

9. Sue this is my long lost brother, said Carl.

10. The judge announced, I now pronounce you Cowboy and Cowgirl!

---

**Extension:** Students in small groups can write their own humorous dialogs. Have them work together to make sure the quotations are correctly punctuated.

Book 3.1/Unit 3
**Pecos Bill**
10

# Using Verb Tenses

**A.** Choose the correct form for each of the following verbs to go with the time clue in the sentence. Mark your answer.

**1.** Tomorrow, Sam _____ home.
ⓐ walks ⓑ walk ⓒ will walk ⓓ walked

**2.** You _____ right now.
ⓐ steers ⓑ will steer ⓒ steered ⓓ steer

**3.** They _____ last night.
ⓐ listened ⓑ listen ⓒ will listen ⓓ listens

**4.** In those days, he _____ behind.
ⓐ lag ⓑ lags ⓒ lagged ⓓ will lag

**B.** Decide if the verb in each sentence should be past tense, present tense, or future tense. Find the verb that correctly completes the sentence. Mark your answer.

**5.** Long ago, Pecos Bill _____ with the other young coyotes.
ⓐ played ⓑ plays ⓒ will play ⓓ plaied

**6.** One day perhaps he _____ to the Southwest.
ⓐ return ⓑ will return ⓒ returns ⓓ returned

**7.** In those days wild horses still _____ the Texas countryside.
ⓐ roam ⓑ roamed ⓒ roams ⓓ will roam

**8.** Tall tales _____ popular today.
ⓐ remained ⓑ remains ⓒ will remain ⓓ remain

# Using Verb Tenses

> • A **present-tense verb** tells what happens now.
>
> • A **past-tense verb** tells about an action that already happened.
>
> • A **future-tense verb** tells about an action that is going to happen.

Work with a partner to correct the sentences below. Each sentence has a verb that is in the wrong tense. As one partner reads each sentence aloud, the other listens to the time clue in the sentence to decide what tense to use. Cross out the verb and write the correct form above it.

1. The store sends the pizza 30 minutes from now.

2. Years ago, coyotes will raise Pecos Bill.

3. Tomorrow, Cookie served lima bean pizza.

4. Right now, the ranch hands pleaded for something different.

5. Yesterday, they dine on beans also.

6. "I now pronounced you Cowboy and Cowgirl!"

7. In the next few minutes, the story ends.

8. Back then, Pecos Bill's pa will need lots of space.

When you are finished, read the sentences aloud. Do the verbs sound correct now?

# Sentence Combining with Verbs

> - Two sentences can be combined by joining the predicates with *and*.
>   Two sentences:      The guests smile. The guests talk.
>   Combined sentence:  The guests <u>smile</u> and <u>talk</u>.

The pairs of sentences below share the same subject. Make them into one sentence by using the word *and* to join the verbs. Write the new sentence on the line.

1. The hotel staff clean. The hotel staff sweep.

   _____

2. The guests laugh. The guests talk.

   _____

3. The cold nips. The cold bites.

   _____

4. The peace and quiet soothes. The peace and quiet relaxes.

   _____

5. The visitors chatter. The visitors shiver.

   _____

6. White, fresh snow glitters. White, fresh snow shines.

   _____

7. The northern lights shimmer. The northern lights glow.

   _____

8. The people gasp. The people stare.

   _____

9. Every spring the hotel melts. Every spring the hotel disappears.

   _____

10. Each winter, a new ice hotel rises. Each winter, a new ice hotel invites.

    _____

**Extension:** Have the students write three or four sentences describing a winter scene. Encourage them to share their descriptions with the class.

# Sentence Combining with Verbs

---

> • Two sentences can be combined by joining the predicates with *and*.
> Two sentences: Guests wear snowsuits. Guests use sleeping bags.
> Combined sentence: <u>Guests wear snowsuits and use sleeping bags</u>.

Underline the predicate in each pair of sentences. Then combine the two sentences and write your one sentence on the line.

**1.** Guests visit Sweden. Guests stay at the Ice Hotel.

_____

**2.** Johan helps the guests. Johan advises them.

_____

**3.** People love the beauty. People enjoy the quiet.

_____

**4.** The northern lights astonish them. The northern lights delight them.

_____

**5.** Kerstin works at the hotel. Kerstin waits on the guests.

_____

**6.** Guests need snowsuits. Guests sleep on ice beds.

_____

**7.** Visitors conquer the cold. Visitors receive a special card.

_____

**8.** The ice melts from the salt. The ice freezes around the string.

_____

---

**Extension:** Have students work with partners. Each student writes pairs of sentences that have the same subject. The partners then join each other's sentences using *and*.

# Sentence Combining with Verbs

> • Two sentences can be combined by joining the predicates with *and*.

Read the sentences below. Rewrite them to join predicates that have the same subjects. Write the combined sentences as a paragraph on the lines.

**1.** The guests arrive slowly. The guests walk into the hotel.

**2.** These people like the cold. These people appreciate winter.

**3.** The staff offers warm snowsuits. The staff issues sleeping bags.

**4.** The hotel covers the ice beds. The hotel recommends exercises for warmth.

**5.** The next day, visitors accept special congratulations. The next day, visitors leave refreshed.

_____

_____

_____

_____

_____

_____

_____

5  Book 3.1/Unit 3
**A Very Cool Place to Visit**

**Extension:** Encourage students to think of details they can add to the paragraph about the ice hotel. Have them write the new paragraph with their additions and if time permits, let them illustrate their work. **91**

## Correcting Sentences

> - Every sentence beings with a capital letter.
> - A statement ends with a period.
> - A question ends with a question mark.
> - A command ends with a period.
> - An exclamation ends with an exclamation point.

Correct each sentence. Write the capital letter over the small letter.
Add the end mark.

1. the hotel is made of ice and snow

2. the hotel is a very cold place

3. can you imagine sleeping on ice

4. can you imagine how strange that is

5. how chilly it is

6. how quiet it is

7. place one end of the string on the ice cube

8. sprinkle salt on the ice cube and string

Combine the predicates of two pairs of sentences above. Write them
on the lines.

9. _____

10. _____

**Extension:** Have students in pairs try the "nice ice experiment."
Ask them to write one of each kind of sentence—statement,
question, command, and exclamation—about the experiment.

92

Book 3.1/Unit 3
**A Very Cool Place to Visit**
10

# Sentence Combining with Verbs

Each pair of sentences below shares a subject. On the line, write the predicate of the first sentence. Then write the word *and* followed by the predicate of the second sentence.

**1.** The guests danced. The guests sang.

_____

**2.** The night sky sparkled. The night sky shone brightly.

_____

**3.** The staff announced dinner. The staff served the guests.

_____

**4.** The cold air stung our faces. The cold air frosted our breath.

_____

Join the sentence pairs below into single sentences. Write your answers.

**5.** A reindeer stands in front. A reindeer greets hotel visitors.

_____

**6.** Snow suits prevent chills. Snow suits allow guests to sleep.

_____

**7.** Guests sleep soundly in their sleeping bags. Guests rise early.

_____

**8.** The hotel boasts 100 ice beds. The hotel attracts many visitors.

_____

**9.** Winter pleases the guests. Winter makes the ice hotel possible.

_____

**10.** Warm weather ruins the ice hotel. Warm weather ends the season.

_____

# Sentence Combining with Verbs

> • Two sentences can be combined by joining the predicates with *and*.

Look at the picture. The paragraph that follows describes what the students are doing. Revise the paragraph by combining sentences. Join the verbs using the word *and*.

> Jerry and Anna lift the ice blocks. Jerry and Anna place them on the wall. Sandra pats snow on the ice. Sandra smoothes the edges. The wall grows longer. The wall reaches higher. Keisha wants a window. Keisha carves it next to the door. The snow melts a little. The snow forms icicles. Doug gets a snack. Doug pours hot chocolate.

Write the new paragraph on the lines below.

_____

_____

_____

_____

_____

**Extension:** Have students in small groups pick a winter sport to describe. Each group should write three or four sentences telling the actions of their sport. Have them check their work for sentences that can be combined.

Book 3.1/Unit 3
**A Very Cool Place to Visit**  6

# Verbs

Read the passage and look at the underlined parts. Is there a better way to say each part? If there is, which is the better way? Mark your answer.

---

<u>A summer storm</u>. Thunder rumbles overhead. <u>Waves crashing on the
(1)                                                                      (2)
shore</u>. Heavy rain is coming to the beach. Let's run for cover!

---

1. ⓐ Summer storm coming!

   ⓑ A summer storm passes by.

   ⓒ A summer storm pass.

   ⓓ No mistake.

2. ⓔ Waves on the shore.

   ⓕ Waves crashes on the shore.

   ⓖ Waves crash on the shore.

   ⓗ No mistake.

---

I didn't see the hailstorm. <u>My sister told me that it is noisy.</u> Hail fell from
                                                         (3)
the sky like rain. It dropped like stone. It hit glass windows. <u>It crashed on
                                                                                        (4)
the ground.</u> She said, "I heard a rumbling sound."

---

3. ⓐ My sister told me that it was noisy.

   ⓑ My sister it was noisy.

   ⓒ It is noisy my sister told me.

   ⓓ No mistake.

4. ⓔ It crashes on the ground.

   ⓕ It crash on the ground.

   ⓖ It's not on the ground.

   ⓗ No mistake.

---

> Yesterday morning, I gather dried leaves in the backyard. By evening, I had finished my lessons. <sup>(5)</sup> Today, I prepare for my tests. I will take them tomorrow. My mom bring me to school.
> <sup>(6)</sup>

**5.** (a) Yesterday morning, I gathered dried leaves in the backyard.

(b) Yesterday morning, I will gather dried leaves in the backyard.

(c) Yesterday morning, I gathers dried leaves in the backyard.

(d) No mistake.

**6.** (e) My mom has brought me to school.

(f) My mom was bringing me to school.

(g) My mom will bring me to school.

(h) No mistake.

> Last summer we went on vacation. We camped in the mountains. My grandmother came with us. She <sup>(7)</sup> brought along her pet dog. It was a cute terrier. It had white fur. When it heard a noise, it barked. We could not sleep from its barking.
> <sup>(8)</sup>

**7.** (a) Last summer, we went camp on vacation in the mountains.

(b) Last summer. We went on vacation in the mountains.

(c) Last summer, we went on vacation and camped in the mountains.

(d) No mistake.

**8.** (e) It was a cute terrier and had white fur.

(f) It was a white fur cute terrier.

(g) It was cute white fur.

(h) No mistake.

# The Verbs *Have* and *Do*

- The verbs *have* and *do* have special forms. The chart shows which form of *have* or *do* to use with a sentence subject.

| SUBJECT | Have PRESENT | PAST | Do PRESENT | PAST |
|---|---|---|---|---|
| he, she, it | has | had | does | did |
| I, we, you, they | have | had | do | did |

Write the correct form of *have* to finish each sentence.

1. The house in the story _____ a thatch roof.

2. Thatch roofs sometimes _____ leaks.

3. This house probably _____ a leak whenever it rains.

4. The father _____ no idea there was a thief on the roof.

5. He _____ no idea there was a wolf outside either.

Write the correct form of *do* to finish each sentence.

6. The wolf _____ not know what a leak is.

7. The thief _____ not know what an eek is.

8. They _____ not know what they're afraid of.

9. What _____ the thief think he fell on?

10. What _____ the wolf think fell on him?

**Extension:** Ask students to write two sentences about the end of the story. Have them use a form of *have* in one sentence and a form of *do* in the other.

# The Verb *Be*

---

- The verb *be* has special forms. The chart shows which form of *be* to use with a sentence subject.

| SUBJECT | PRESENT | PAST |
|---|---|---|
| *he, she, it* | *is* | *was* |
| *we, you, they* | *are* | *were* |
| *I* | *am* | *was* |

Write the correct form of *be* to finish each sentence.

**1.** "The Terrible Eek" _____ a funny story.

**2.** The father says, "I _____ most afraid of a leak."

**3.** A wolf _____ outside and heard him.

**4.** He thought, "What _____ a leak?"

**5.** A thief _____ on the roof and heard him.

**6.** He thought, "What _____ an eek?"

**7.** They _____ both afraid.

**8.** They told other animals, and they _____ afraid, too.

**9.** At the end, they all _____ so scared they run away.

**10.** What _____ your favorite stories?

---

**Extension:** Have students draw a picture of their favorite character in the story and write a sentence telling who the character in the picture is.

Name_____ Date_____

# The Verbs *Have*, *Do*, and *Be*

---

> • The verbs *have*, *do,* and *be* have special forms.

Write the correct form of the given verb to finish each sentence.

**1.** have    The wolf _____ an eerie howl.

**2.** have    Tigers _____ an awful roar.

**3.** have    The monkey _____ a terrible screech.

**4.** be       They make those sounds when they _____ scared.

**5.** be       They _____ scared when they saw the thief.

**6.** be       They thought he _____ the leak.

**7.** be       The noise they made _____ awful!

**8.** do       _____ they run away?

**9.** do       Yes, they _____!

**10.** do     What sound _____ an owl make?

---

**Extension:** Have partners take turns using forms of *have, do,* and *be* in sentences about story characters. One says a sentence that tells about the present. The other makes the sentence tell about the past.

## Correcting a Letter

> • Begin the greeting and closing with a capital letter.
>
> • Use a comma after the greeting.
>
> • Use a comma after the closing.
>
> • Use a comma between the names of a city and a state.
>
> • Use a comma between the day and year in a date.

Add the correct punctuation and capitalization to this letter. Be sure that all the forms of *have, do,* and *be* are correct. Write the letter correctly.

April 1 2005

dear Family

    I hope you are well. I am not. I have the most awful experience! Last night I were face to face with the terrible eek. It is awful! I am sure it was a punishment. I do not wish to be a thief anymore.

your son

The Thief

# The Verbs *Have*, *Do*, and *Be*

Choose the correct word to complete each sentence.

**1.** This _____ what happens in the story.

  ⓐ are      ⓑ were      ⓒ is      ⓓ has

**2.** The father says he _____ afraid of leaks.

  ⓐ had      ⓑ is      ⓒ am      ⓓ was

**3.** He means he _____ not want the roof to leak.

  ⓐ do      ⓑ does      ⓒ did      ⓓ was

**4.** The wolf thinks a leak _____ a fearsome beast.

  ⓐ has      ⓑ is      ⓒ have      ⓓ does

**5.** So _____ the thief.

  ⓐ do      ⓑ does      ⓒ is      ⓓ was

**6.** They think it _____ an awful screech.

  ⓐ have      ⓑ be      ⓒ has      ⓓ were

**7.** They both _____ very scared.

  ⓐ have      ⓑ is      ⓒ had      ⓓ are

**8.** They _____ not want to stay there!

  ⓐ does      ⓑ are      ⓒ were      ⓓ do

# The Verbs *Have*, *Do*, and *Be*

- The verbs *have*, *do*, and *be* have special forms.

**Mechanics:**

- Begin the greeting and closing with a capital letter.
- Use a comma after the greeting.
- Use a comma after the closing.
- Use a comma between the names of a city and a state.
- Use a comma between the day and year in a date.

The writer of this letter didn't check it over for mistakes. As you read the letter, correct any capitalization and punctuation errors you find. Look for mistakes made with the verbs *have*, *do*, and *be*.

1020 broad street
El Paso Texas 79512

August 25 2000

dear Matt

These last two weeks has gone really fast. I does not believe summer's almost over, and I'll be home in just a few days.

Do school start before or after Labor Day? If it are after, maybe we can visit my friend in Chicago Illinois.

Take care. I'll see you on September 6 2000 in Gary Indiana.

your friend

Danny

# Linking Verbs

- A **linking verb** does not show action. It connects the subject to the rest of the sentence.
- The word *be* is a common linking verb. *Be* has special forms in the present tense.
  I am happy to be here.
  This party is very nice.
  All my friends are here.

Write *am*, *is*, or *are* to finish each sentence.

1. I _____ fascinated by horned toads.

2. They _____ shaped like frogs.

3. But they _____ really toads.

4. A horned toad's body _____ covered with horns.

5. My sister's name _____ Maria.

6. It _____ her birthday.

7. We _____ having a party.

8. Our aunts and uncles _____ here.

9. Our cousins _____ here, too.

10. I _____ happy to see everyone.

**Extension:** Have children write three sentences about something that fascinates them or makes them happy.

# Linking Verbs

---

> • The verb *be* is a common linking verb. *Be* has special forms in the past tense.
> The band was playing.
> My mother and father were dancing.

Finish each sentence with *was* or *were*.

**1.** We _____ having a birthday party.

**2.** The children _____ trying to hit the piñata.

**3.** The grown-ups _____ laughing and talking.

**4.** Grandma _____ holding the baby.

**5.** My father _____ cooking at the barbecue.

**6.** I _____ waiting for my mother to cut the cake.

**7.** It _____ chocolate, my favorite kind.

**8.** It _____ covered with sweet icing.

**9.** There _____ nine candles on it, too.

**10.** It _____ my ninth birthday.

---

**Extension:** Write two or three sentences telling about a birthday party you remember.

Book 3.2/Unit 1
**In My Family** /10

# Linking Verbs

---

- The verb *be* is a linking verb. It connects the subject to the rest of the sentence.

- *Be* has special forms in the present tense and the past tense.

| PRESENT | PAST |
|---------|------|
| I am writing a story. | I was born in Mexico. |
| It is about my family. | My mother and father were born |
| They are my favorite people. | there, too. |

Write the correct form of the verb *be* to finish each sentence.

1. Yesterday I _____ eight years old.

2. Today I _____ nine.

3. My cousin _____ nine, too.

4. His birthday _____ last week.

5. We _____ babies together.

6. Now we _____ best friends.

7. His mother _____ my mother's sister.

8. They _____ born on the very same day.

9. Our mothers _____ twins!

10. I _____ always sure which twin is my mother.

---

**Extension:** Have students work with a partner. Each one writes three sentences in the present tense using *am*, *is*, and *are*. Then they rewrite each other's sentences in the past tense.

# Using Capital Letters

- A proper noun begins with a capital letter.
- The name of a day, month, or holiday begins with a capital letter.
- An abbreviation begins with a capital letter and ends with a period.
- Abbreviate most titles of people before names.

Read this journal entry.

Cross out the incorrect linking verbs and write the right ones.

Add capital letters.

Add a period to each abbreviation.

feb 14

Today was valentine's day. We had a little party at school. We had cupcakes that aaron's mom made. They was decorated with candy hearts. Then ms Garcia passed out the valentines. I got a nice one from felicia. I gave her a nice one, too. that's because we is best friends. Then we had a spelling quiz because it was friday.

**Extension:** Have children make a list that includes everyone's birthday and the holidays your class celebrates.

# Linking Verbs

Write the linking verb in each sentence.

1. Making empanadas is an annual event. _____

2. Empanadas are sweet turnovers. _____

3. They are filled with sweet potato or squash. _____

4. Last year was a good year for squash. _____

5. So there were more empanadas than ever. _____

Choose a verb from the box to complete each sentence.

| am | is | are | was | were |
|----|----|-----|-----|------|

6. My mother _____ a good cook.

7. I _____ a good cook, too.

8. These _____ cookies that I baked.

9. Yesterday there _____ two dozen of them.

10. My brother _____ greedy and ate too many.

# Linking Verbs

---

The verb *be* connects the subject to the rest of the sentence. *Be* has special forms in the present tense and the past tense.

| PRESENT | PAST |
|---------|------|
| I **am** | I **was** |
| He, she, it **is** | He, she, it **was** |
| They, we **are** | They, we **were** |

**Mechanics:**

• A proper noun begins with a capital letter.

• The name of a day, month, or holiday begins with a capital letter.

• An abbreviation begins with a capital letter and ends with a period.

• Abbreviate most titles of people before names.

---

Read each sentence aloud. Correct the linking verb. Write the sentence with the correct capital letters.

**1.** Next thursday was arbor day.

_____

**2.** Our class are going to plant a tree.

_____

**3.** We was going to buy it on tuesday.

_____

**4.** Our teacher, ms Pratt, were going with us.

_____

**5.** My classmates and I am excited about it.

_____

# Helping Verbs

> • A **helping verb** helps another verb show an action. *Have, has,* and *had* are helping verbs. They help to tell about things that have already happened.
> My aunt has moved to the desert.
> She had visited there before.
> We have asked her to invite us there.

Write *have, has,* or *had* to complete each sentence.

1. Many changes _____ occurred in the desert.

2. A woodpecker _____ moved into that cactus.

3. Another cactus _____ toppled over.

4. The wind _____ pushed one over before.

5. Many birds _____ lived in that cactus.

6. Now they _____ moved to other homes.

7. A scorpion and some ants _____ moved in.

8. A tall cactus _____ started to grown an arm.

9. That cactus _____ started out as a tiny seed.

10. But a hundred years _____ passed since then.

**Extension:** Have students work in pairs. Ask each student to write two sentences that contain helping verbs. Then have them underline the helping verbs in the other's sentences.

# Helping Verbs

---

- *Is, are, am, was, were,* and *will* are also helping verbs.

- *Is, are,* and *am* help to tell about what is happening now.
  I am reading about coyotes.
  Nick is reading about coyotes.
  We are reading about coyotes.

- *Was* and *were* help to tell about what was happening in the past.
  I was reading about scorpions yesterday.
  We were reading about scorpions yesterday.

- *Will* helps to tell about something that will happen.
  We will read about pack rats tomorrow.

Write a helping verb to finish each sentence.

**1.** Last night I _____ talking to Grandma on the phone.

**2.** We _____ talking about our visit.

**3.** She _____ telling me about the desert.

**4.** Mom and I _____ going to the desert on vacation.

**5.** Grandma _____ living there now.

**6.** We _____ spend the winter holidays with her.

**7.** We _____ planning to stay for two weeks.

**8.** Mom _____ taking time off from work.

**9.** I _____ taking an extra day off from school.

**10.** As we talked, I _____ getting more excited.

---

**Extension:** Write three sentences that have helping verbs. Tell about a visit your family has made.

Book 3.2/Unit 1
**Cactus Hotel**
10

# Helping Verbs

> • A helping verb helps another verb show an action.
>
> • Forms of *have—have, has,* and *had—*are used with verbs with *-ed*. The seed had dropped off the pack rat's whiskers.
>
> • Forms of *be—is, are, was,* and *were—*are used with verbs with *-ing*. Seeds are dropping from the pack rat's whiskers.
>
> • *Will* helps to tell what will happen in the future. A cactus will grow from that seed.

Write the helping verb that completes each sentence.

**1.** It _____ rained for many days.

**2.** A cactus _____ growing slowly.

**3.** Its long roots _____ pulling in water.

**4.** But now the rain _____ stopped.

**5.** The desert _____ blooming with color.

**6.** Yellow-and-white flowers _____ appeared on the cactus.

**7.** Birds and bees _____ buzzing around.

**8.** Bats _____ come later for the nectar.

**9.** Ants _____ crawling in the cactus spines.

**10.** The cactus _____ grow for a hundred years.

**10** Book 3.2/Unit 1
**Cactus Hotel**

**Extension:** Have students find two sentences with helping verbs in "Cactus Hotel."

**111**

# Writing Book Titles

> • Begin the first word and each important word in a book title with a capital letter.
>
> • Underline the title of a book.

Rewrite each of these sentences. Write book titles correctly. Use the correct helping verb.

**1.** I has read james and the giant peach.

_____

**2.** Now I am reading ben and me.

_____

**3.** At school, we was reading sarah, plain and tall.

_____

**4.** Next we will read the cricket in times square.

_____

**5.** My sister has always loved charlotte's web.

_____

**6.** My brother has read the shrinking of treehorn.

_____

**7.** Our class has read the wreck of the zephyr.

_____

**8.** Has you read cloudy with a chance of meatballs?

_____

**112**

**Extension:** Write the titles of three of your favorite books.

Book 3.2/Unit 1
**Cactus Hotel** 8

# Helping Verbs

Write the helping verb in each sentence.

**1.** The young pack rat had scurried off. _____

**2.** The jackrabbit has disappeared into a hole. _____

**3.** The ants were climbing on the cactus. _____

**4.** The rains have stopped. _____

**5.** Soon the sun will rise. _____

Choose a helping verb from the box to complete each sentence.

| am | is | are | was | were |
|---|---|---|---|---|

**6.** Yesterday we _____ reading about the desert.

**7.** Jason _____ absent.

**8.** Today we _____ painting pictures of it.

**9.** Jason _____ painting a scorpion.

**10.** I _____ painting cactus flowers.

# Helping Verbs

---

- **Helping verbs** help other verbs show an action.
- Forms of *have*—*have*, *has*, and *had*—are used with verbs with *-ed*.
- Forms of *be*—*is*, *are*, *was*, and *were*—are used with verbs with *-ing*.
- *Will* helps to tell what will happen in the future.

**Mechanics:**

- Begin the first word and each important word in a book title with a capital letter.
- Underline the title of a book.

Rewrite the sentence about each picture. Use the correct helping verb and the correct form of *read*. Write the book title correctly.

**1.** Megan is sit inside an airplane.

_____

**2.** Megan are read ramona and her father.

_____

**3.** Zack are borrow a book.

_____

**4.** Zack will reading nate the great.

_____

**5.** Jen were read freaky Friday when the phone rang.

_____

# Irregular Verbs

• An **irregular verb** has a special spelling to show the past tense.

| PRESENT | PAST |
|---------|------|
| I *do* | I *did* |
| You *see* | You *saw* |
| He *comes* | He *came* |
| We *go* | We *went* |
| They *bring* | They *brought* |

Rewrite these sentences in the past tense.

**1.** The whale comes to the surface to breathe.

_____

**2.** The people on the boat see the whale.

_____

**3.** The blue whale does not have any teeth.

_____

**4.** It does not need teeth.

_____

**5.** The whale goes south for the winter.

_____

**Extension:** Have students work in pairs. Ask each student to write a sentence in the present tense using *do, see, come, go,* or *bring.* Then have students rewrite their partner's sentence in the past tense.

# Irregular Verbs

- An irregular verb has a special spelling to show the past tense.
- Some irregular verbs have a special spelling when used with the helping verb *have*.

| PRESENT | PAST | PAST |
|---|---|---|
| I *do* | I *did* | I have *done* |
| you *see* | you *saw* | you have *seen* |
| she *comes* | she *came* | she has *come* |
| we *go* | we *went* | we have *gone* |
| they *bring* | they *brought* | they have *brought* |
| I *run* | I *ran* | I have *run* |
| he *gives* | he *gave* | he has *given* |
| we *sing* | we *sang* | we have *sung* |
| they *begin* | they *began* | they have *begun* |
| I *eat* | I *ate* | I have *eaten* |
| it *grows* | it *grew* | it has *grown* |

Write the correct form of the verb to finish the sentence.

**1.** come    A whale _____ to the surface.

**2.** run    We all _____ to see it.

**3.** see    Have you ever _____ a blue whale?

**4.** eat    The whale _____ krill all summer.

**5.** grow    It had _____ a thick layer of fat.

**6.** eat    Over the winter, the whale had _____ very little.

**7.** give    The whale had _____ birth to a baby.

**8.** sing    The whale _____ its special song.

**9.** begin    The whale had _____ its journey south.

**10.** go    Last fall, all the whales _____ south.

**Extension:** Have students find other examples of irregular verbs in books and magazines.

Book 3.2/Unit 1
**Big Blue Whale**
10

Name_____ Date_____ **Grammar** (117)

# Irregular Verbs

---

- An irregular verb has a special spelling to show the past tense.
- Some irregular verbs have a special spelling when used with the helping verb *have*.

---

Rewrite these sentences in the past tense.

**1.** The whale eats tons of krill.

_____

**2.** Whales from the South Pole go north.

_____

**3.** The whale grows a thick layer of fat.

_____

**4.** The mother whale gives birth to a baby.

_____

**5.** After a year, the baby begins life on its own.

_____

Finish each sentence with the correct past-tense form of the verb.

**6.** They have _____ something special.          did          done

**7.** They have _____ a whale.          saw          seen

**8.** They _____ to the beach.          ran          run

**9.** They _____ their binoculars with them.          brang     brought

**10.** We had _____ the song before.          sang          sung

---

10  Book 3.2/Unit 1
**Big Blue Whale**          **Extension:** Have students write sentences using the
past and past-with-*have* tenses of *take*.          **117**

# Dialogue and Quotation Marks

---

> • Use **quotation marks** at the beginning and end of a person's exact words.
>
> • Use a comma after the name of a person being spoken to.
>
> • Use a comma after the words *yes* and *no* when they begin a sentence.

Write each line of dialogue correctly. Use the correct form of the irregular verb.

**1.** Mr. Holland have you ever saw a blue whale?  asked Arnold.

_____

**2.** No  I have not seen a blue whale  said Mr. Holland  but I have saw a gray whale.

_____

_____

**3.** Where did you seen it? asked Arnold.

_____

**4.** I had gone on a whale-watching cruise said Mr. Holland.

_____

**5.** Did you take a picture? asked Arnold.

_____

---

**Extension:** Have students write another question and answer for the dialogue.

Book 3.2/Unit 1
**Big Blue Whale**  5

# Irregular Verbs

Choose the verb form that goes with *have*. Mark your answer.

**1.** We had _____ on a whale-watching cruise.

ⓐ gone      ⓑ go      © went

**2.** The captain had _____ us a wonderful tour.

ⓐ given      ⓑ gave      © give

**3.** Time had almost _____ out.

ⓐ run      ⓑ runned      © ran

**4.** We had still not _____ a whale.

ⓐ saw      ⓑ seen      © see

Choose the correct past tense form.

**5.** The whale _____ krill all summer.

ⓐ eaten      ⓑ eat      © ate

**6.** The whale _____ south for the winter.

ⓐ went      ⓑ gone      © go

**7.** There the whale _____ birth to a baby.

ⓐ given      ⓑ give      © gave

**8.** Mother and baby _____ back to the polar seas in the spring.

ⓐ come      ⓑ came      © comen

**9.** The baby whale _____ up in less than a year.

ⓐ grown      ⓑ grow      © grew

**10.** The next fall, it _____ living on its own.

ⓐ begun      ⓑ began      © begin

# Irregular Verbs

---

- An irregular verb has a special spelling to show the past tense.
- Some irregular have a special spelling when used with the helping verb *have*.

**Mechanics:**

- Use quotation marks at the beginning and end of a person's exact words.
- Use a comma after the name of a person being spoken to.
- Use a comma after the words *Yes* and *No* when they begin a sentence.

Read each sentence aloud. Then rewrite the sentence using the correct form of the verb and adding quotation marks and commas.

**I.** We goed on a whale-watching boat said Nick.

_____

**2.** The trip beginned early in the morning said Carly.

_____

**3.** The boat bringed us far out to sea said Carly.

_____

**4.** We seed a whole pod of gray whales said Nick.

_____

**5.** Alex have you ever doed that? asked Carly.

_____

**6.** Yes I have goed on a trip like that said Alex.

_____

**7.** My grandma gived us tickets for a trip last year said Alex.

_____

**8.** Grandma even comed along with us said Alex.

---

# Contractions

> • A **contraction** is a shortened form of two words.
>
> • An **apostrophe** (') shows where one or more letters have been left out.
>
> isn't      is not
> aren't     are not
> wasn't    was not
> weren't   were not

Write the contraction that can take the place of the underlined words.

1. Whales <u>are not</u> fish. _____

2. A whale <u>is not</u> able to breathe underwater. _____

3. The baby whale <u>was not</u> well. _____

4. She <u>was not</u> more than a week old. _____

5. Her mother <u>was not</u> with her. _____

6. The animal-rescue workers <u>were not</u> sure what to do. _____

7. The scientists <u>were not</u> sure what to feed her. _____

8. J.J.'s story <u>is not</u> over. _____

9. She <u>is not</u> at Sea World anymore. _____

10. She is back in the ocean, but scientists <u>are not</u> sure where. _____

10 Book 3.2/Unit 1
J.J.'s Big Day

**Extension:** Have children use one of the contractions
to write a sentence about whales.

121

# Contraction

- A contraction is a shortened form of two words.

- An apostrophe (') shows where one or more letters have been left out. In most contractions with *not*, the apostrophe takes the place of *o*.

  hasn't     has not     don't      do not
  haven't    have not    doesn't    does not
  hadn't     had not     didn't     did not

  *Can't* and *won't* are different. The apostrophe in *can't* takes the place of two letters: *no*. In *won't*, three letters disappear and the *o* changes position.

  can't      can not     won't      will not

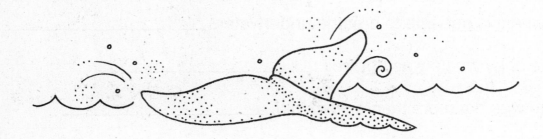

Find the contraction in each sentence. Write the two words that form the contraction.

**1.** Whales don't have gills. _____

**2.** They can't breathe underwater. _____

**3.** A whale's tail doesn't move like a fish's tail. _____

**4.** Most people haven't seen a whale. _____

**5.** The average person hasn't rescued one. _____

**6.** Scientist didn't know what happened to J.J.'s mother. _____

**7.** If humans hadn't helped, J.J. would have died. _____

**8.** We probably won't ever know if J.J. is all right. _____

**Extension:** Have students work in pairs. Ask each student to write two sentences using contractions. Then have them identify the contractions in their partner's sentences and write the two words that form each contraction.

**122**

Book 3.2/Unit 1
**J.J.'s Big Day**

8

# Contractions

> - A **contraction** is a shortened form of two words.
> - An **apostrophe** (') shows where one or more letters have been left out. In most contractions with *not*, the apostrophe takes the place of *o*.

Rewrite each sentence using a contraction in place of the underlined verb. Make the sentence mean the opposite.

1. Gray whales <u>are</u> as big as blue whales.

   _____

2. An elephant <u>is</u> as big as a blue whale.

   _____

3. A baleen whale <u>does</u> have teeth.

   _____

4. A baby whale <u>can</u> survive without its mother.

   _____

5. J.J.'s mother <u>was</u> nearby.

   _____

6. The scientists <u>did</u> know what to do.

   _____

7. They <u>had</u> fed a baby whale before.

   _____

8. Returning J.J. to the ocean <u>was</u> easy.

   _____

9. The scientists <u>were</u> sure what would happen.

   _____

10. They <u>have</u> returned many whales to the ocean.

   _____

**Extension:** Ask students to write a sentence that includes a linking verb or a helping verb. Then have them turn the sentence into one that means the opposite by replacing the verb with a verb + *not* contraction. **123**

# Using Apostrophes

> - An **apostrophe** takes the place of letters left out of a contraction.
> - Add an apostrophe and *s* to a singular noun to make it possessive.
> - Add an apostrophe to make most plural nouns possessive.
> - Add an apostrophe and *s* to form the possessive of plural nouns that do not end with *s*.

Rewrite these sentences adding apostrophes where they are needed.

1. A whales tail isnt like a fishs tail.

   _____

2. Big whales mouths arent full of teeth.

   _____

3. The baby whales name is J.J.

   _____

4. J.J.s baby food was like her mothers milk.

   _____

5. The scientists job wasnt easy.

   _____

6. J.J. didnt know how to find her own food.

   _____

7. She hadnt been with other whales.

   _____

8. The keepers hand stroked J.J.s bumpy nose.

   _____

9. A childrens magazine reported the baby whales story.

   _____

10. J.J.s story touched peoples hearts.

   _____

**Extension:** Invite students to write sentences that retell their favorite part of J.J.'s story. Remind them to use apostrophes correctly in their sentences.

# Contractions

Write the contraction for each pair of words.

**1.** does not _____

**2.** will not _____

**3.** can not _____

**4.** have not _____

**5.** are not _____

**6.** did not _____

**7.** is not _____

**8.** do not _____

Write the words that form the contraction in each sentence.

**9.** J.J. hadn't been with other whales. _____

**10.** Whales can't breathe underwater. _____

**11.** Scientists weren't sure what to feed J.J. _____

**12.** J.J. wasn't a blue whale. _____

# Contractions

> A **contraction** is a shortened form of two words.
>
> An **apostrophe** (') shows where one or more letters have been left out.

- An apostrophe takes the place of letters left out of a contraction.
- Add an apostrophe and *s* to a singular noun to make it possessive.
- Add an apostrophe to make most plural nouns possessive.
- Add an apostrophe and *s* to form the possessive of plural nouns that do not end with *s*.

Add the apostrophes in these sentences that tell about the picture.
Write the contraction on the line.

**1.** This isnt a sight you see every day. _____

**2.** Its the picture of a whale. _____

**3.** Whales arent fish. _____

**4.** They cant breathe underwater. _____

**5.** Theyll come to the surface to breathe. _____

**6.** Theyve blowholes that are like nostrils. _____

**7.** Theyre located on top of their heads. _____

**8.** Wed like to go whale watching. _____

# More Verbs

Read the passage and look at the underlined section. Is there a mistake? If there is, how do you correct it? Mark your answer.

---

When we arrived, the dolphins was starting a show. I was watching a
                                      (1)
dolphin catch a ball when my brother ran to the stairs. My father saw me
chase him. Everyone was clapping when we returned. The dolphin show
                                      (2)
had ended.

---

1. ⓐ Change *was* to *is*.
   ⓑ Change *was* to *am*.
   ⓒ Change *was* to *were*.
   ⓓ No mistake.

2. ⓔ Change *was* to *is*.
   ⓕ Change *was* to *am*.
   ⓖ Change *was* to *were*.
   ⓗ No mistake.

---

Making empanadas are an annual event. Empanadas are sweet
                      (3)
turnovers made from squash. Last year is a good year for squash. So
                                      (4)
there were more empanadas than ever.

---

3. ⓐ Change *are* to *is*.
   ⓑ Change *are* to *was*.
   ⓒ Change *are* to *were*.
   ⓓ No mistake.

4. ⓔ Change *is* to *are*.
   ⓕ Change *is* to *was*.
   ⓖ Change *is* to *were*.
   ⓗ No mistake.

---

---

We had gone on a whale-watching cruise. <u>The captain given us a</u>
<u>wonderful tour.</u> He told us that whales went south for the winter. <u>Mother</u>
<u>and baby whales comes back to the polar seas in the spring.</u>
(5)
(6)

---

**5.** (a) Change *given* to *gives*.

   (b) Change *given* to *had given*.

   (c) Change *given* to *was given*.

   (d) No mistake.

**6.** (e) Change *comes* to *coming*.

   (f) Change *comes* to *comed*.

   (g) Change *comes* to *came*.

   (h) No mistake.

---

J.J. was found on a California beach one day. <u>J.J. weren't a blue whale.</u>
The baby gray whale was sick and hungry. <u>Scientists wasn't sure what to</u>
<u>feed J.J.</u>
(7)
(8)

---

**7.** (a) Change *weren't* to *wasn't*.

   (b) Change *weren't* to *hasn't*.

   (c) Change *weren't* to *don't*.

   (d) No mistake.

**8.** (e) Change *wasn't* to *isn't*.

   (f) Change *wasn't* to *weren't*.

   (g) Change *wasn't* to *haven't*.

   (h) No mistake.

---

# Singular Pronouns

> - A **pronoun** is a word that takes the place of one or more nouns.
>
> - A pronoun must match the noun that it replaces.
>   Singular pronouns are *I, you, he, she, it, me, him, her.*
>   <u>"Lon Po Po"</u> is a folk tale. <u>It</u> is a folk tale.

Read the sentences. Write the pronoun or pronouns you find in each sentence.

**1.** Ann read <u>Lon Po Po</u> to James and me. _____

**2.** She says the story is a folk tale. _____

**3.** Ed Young wrote it. _____

**4.** He heard the tale as a child. _____

**5.** I wonder who told the tale to him? _____

**6.** Have you heard the tale before? _____

**7.** Ann says <u>Lon Po Po</u> reminds her of <u>Little Red Riding Hood.</u> _____

**8.** I agree with her. _____

**Extension:** Have students work in pairs. Ask each student to write an original sentence using singular pronouns. Have students trade sentences and underline the pronouns.

# Plural Pronouns

> • **Plural pronouns** are *we, you, they, us, them.*

Read each pair of sentences. Replace the underlined word or words with the correct pronoun.

1. <u>James and I</u> listened to the story of "Lon Po Po." _____

2. I'm glad Ann read it to <u>James and me</u>. _____

3. Do <u>you and your friends</u> know the story? _____

4. In the story, a wolf tries to trick <u>Tao, Paotze, and Shang</u>. _____

5. <u>Tao, Paotze, and Shang</u> were told to latch the door. _____

6. The wolf asked <u>the children</u> to open the door. _____

7. <u>Tao and Paotze</u> could hardly wait to see their Po Po. _____

8. The cunning wolf walked past <u>the girls</u>. _____

9. <u>My friends and I</u> knew the girls were in danger. _____

10. Shang told <u>her sisters</u> that Po Po was really a wolf. _____

**Extension:** On index cards write plural subject and object pronouns. Invite students to choose a card and then write a sentence using the pronoun.

130

Book 3.2/Unit 2
Lon Po Po
10

Name_____ Date_____

# Singular and Plural Pronouns

---

- A **pronoun** is a word that takes the place of one or more nouns.

- A pronoun must match the noun that it replaces.

- Singular pronouns are *I, you, he, she, it, me, him, her*.

- Plural pronouns are *we, you, they, us, them*.

---

Write the correct pronoun for the underlined noun or nouns.

**1.** Is "<u>Lon Po Po</u>" a story from China? _____

**2.** <u>The wolf</u> pretends to be an old woman. _____

**3.** Do <u>Tao, Paotze, and Shang</u> live in the city or in the country? _____

**4.** <u>The mother</u> is visiting the girls' grandmother. _____

**5.** The wolf tricks <u>Tao and Paotze</u> at first. _____

**6.** Does the wolf fool <u>Shang</u>? _____

**7.** Do <u>wolves</u> frighten you? _____

**8.** Do <u>you and your classmates</u> like the story? _____

---

**Extension:** Have students work in pairs. Ask each student to write two questions about "Lon Po Po." Have children trade questions and answer each one using pronouns wherever possible.

**131**

# Pronouns with Capital Letters

---

- Use a comma before *and* when you join two sentences.

Read the paragraph. Find the mistakes. Then write the paragraph correctly. Improve the paragraph by joining the underlined sentences with *and*.

My sister and i just finished reading "Lon Po Po." We like the story. She thinks "Lon Po Po" is better than "Little Red Riding Hood." She and i agree about that! Us both liked how the girls tricked the wolf. At first i didn't think they knew that Lon Po Po wasn't really their grandmother. It's a good thing Shang was smarter than the wolf.

_____

_____

_____

_____

_____

_____

_____

# Pronouns

**A.** Write **yes** if the underlined word is a pronoun. Write **no** if the underlined word is not a pronoun.

1. Shang asked the wolf, "Have <u>you</u> eaten nuts?" _____

2. The wolf hadn't, so Shang said she'd get <u>him</u> some. _____

3. Tao and Paotze went <u>along</u> with her to the tree. _____

4. When the <u>three</u> got to the tree, Shang told them about the wolf. _____

5. <u>They</u> climbed up the tree and waited. _____

6. After a while, the <u>wolf</u> called to them. _____

**B.** Underline the pronoun in each sentence. Then write **S** if it is singular or **P** if it is plural.

7. Shang said, "We are on top of the tree eating nuts." _____

8. The wolf said, "Please get me some nuts, too." _____

9. Shang said, "Po Po, you must come and pick the nuts." _____

10. The girls pulled, and then they dropped the basket. _____

## Pronouns

---

- A **pronoun** is a word that takes the place of one or more nouns.

  A pronoun must match the noun that it replaces.

  Singular pronouns are *I, you, he, she, it, me, him, her*.

  Plural pronouns are *we, you, they, us, them*.

---

Look at the pictures. Read the sentences. Replace the underlined word with the correct pronoun and write each sentence.

**1.** <u>Him</u> pretended to be Po Po.

_____

**2.** <u>Her</u> was the girls' grandmother.

_____

**3.** <u>Them</u> were home alone.

_____

**4.** Mother went to visit <u>she</u>.

_____

**5.** He knocked on the door and said, "Let <u>I</u> in."

_____

**6.** They opened <u>its</u>.

_____

**7.** The wolf tricked <u>they</u>.

_____

**8.** In the end, they outsmart <u>he</u>.

_____

**Extension:** Have students work with a partner. Ask one student to write a
sentence telling what mother brings back for the girls from the real Po
**134** Po. Ask the other student to rewrite the sentence using the pronouns.

Book 3.2/Unit 2
**Lon Po Po** 8

# Subject Pronouns

---

> • Use a **subject pronoun** as the subject of a sentence.
>
>   *I, you, he, she, it, we,* and *they* are subject pronouns.

Read the sentences. Choose the correct pronoun in ( ) to complete each sentence. Write the pronoun.

**1.** My brother, sister, and _____ get a nature magazine.    (me, I)

**2.** _____ comes every month.    (It, Its)

**3.** _____ each like different things about the magazine.    (Us, We)

**4.** _____ enjoys the fun pages.    (Her, She)

**5.** _____ just read about porcupines.    (Him, He)

**6.** Do _____ know anything about them?    (you, your)

**7.** _____ have quills with sharp barbs on the ends.    (Them, They)

**8.** Is _____ true that they can shoot their quills?    (it, it's)

---

8 | Book 3.2/Unit 2
**Animal Fact/Animal Fable**

**Extension:** Have students write sentences that describe two different animals. Tell them that each sentence should begin with a subject pronoun. Have them trade sentences and rewrite them, replacing each pronoun with a noun.

**135**

# Object Pronouns

> • Use an **object pronoun** after an action verb or after a word such as
> *for, at, of, with,* or *to.*
> *Me, you, him, her, it, us,* and *them* are object pronouns.

Read the sentences. Choose the correct word in ( ) to complete each
sentence. Write the word.

**1.** My brother went for a walk with _____.                    (I, me)

**2.** I caught a cricket for _____.                              (he, him)

**3.** What can we put _____ in?                                 (its, it)

**4.** I showed the cricket to my mother and
asked _____ for some ideas.                                      (she, her)

**5.** She gave _____ two berry baskets and some twist ties.     (us, we)

**6.** We used the ties to fasten _____ together to              (they, them)
make a cage.

**7.** Then we put some leaves and twigs in _____.               (it's, it)

**8.** I took some cucumber slices and put _____ in the cage.    (they, them)

**9.** Dad told _____ about the difference between
a cricket's chirps on a hot day and on a cool day.                 (we, us)

**10.** We can tell _____ all about it.                          (you, your)

**Extension:** Invite students to choose a paragraph from
a story or article about an animal and identify all the
**136**    object pronouns.

Book 3.2/Unit 2
**Animal Fact/Animal Fable**   /10

# Subject and Object Pronouns

- Use a **subject pronoun** as the subject of a sentence.
  *I, you, he, she, it, we,* and *they* are subject pronouns.
- Use an **object pronoun** after an action verb or after a word such as
  *for, at, of, with,* or *to.*
  *Me, you, him, her, it, us,* and *them* are object pronouns.

Replace the underlined word or words in each sentence with the
correct subject or object pronoun. Write the new sentences.

1. My parents took my sister and me to a zoo.

_____

2. A sign says that visitors can pet and feed the animals.

_____

3. My sister fed crackers to a baby goat.

_____

4. Two more goats came along and nibbled at her shirt.

_____

5. My dad lifted my sister up to get away from the goats.

_____

6. Dad laughed and said to my sister, "Goats eat just about everything!"

_____

7. My mom took a picture of my sister and the goats.

_____

8. Do you and your friends want to see the picture?

_____

8  Book 3.2/Unit 2
Animal Fact/Animal Fable

**Extension:** Have students work in pairs. Ask each student to write a short paragraph about an animal. Have students trade papers. Ask them to underline all the subject and object pronouns.

**137**

# Writing the Pronouns *I* and *Me*

- Always write the pronoun *I* with a capital letter.
- *I* and *me* come last if joined by *and* with another pronoun or a noun.

Proofread the paragraph. Then write it correctly.

Father asked me and my brother, "have you ever found an empty turtle shell?" i and my brother tried to find one, but we couldn't. i and he found out that the shell is part of the turtle's body, and the turtle will die without it. i will never try to take a turtle out of its shell. i and you should not paint the turtle's shell.

_____

_____

_____

_____

_____

_____

# Subject and Object Pronouns

Read the first sentence of each set. One of the four sentences that follows correctly replaces the underlined words. Mark the correct sentence.

1. Our dog Misty speaks to us but not with words.
   ⓐ They speak to me but not with words.
   ⓑ You speak to her but not with words.
   ⓒ She speaks to us but not with words.
   ⓓ It speaks to me but not with words.

2. Dogs use their tails to speak to humans!
   ⓐ Dogs use them to speak to us!
   ⓑ Dogs use it to speak to us!
   ⓒ Them use their tails to speak to humans!
   ⓓ They use their tails to speak to humans!

3. My father knows when Misty is happy.
   ⓐ He knows when Misty is happy.
   ⓑ We know when she is happy.
   ⓒ I know when Misty is happy.
   ⓓ You know she is happy.

4. A porcupine surprised our dog Misty one afternoon.
   ⓐ It surprised our dog Misty one afternoon.
   ⓑ A porcupine surprised them one afternoon.
   ⓒ A porcupine surprised her one afternoon.
   ⓓ They surprised us one afternoon.

5. Misty barked and barked at the porcupine.
   ⓐ Misty barked and barked at us.
   ⓑ Misty barked and barked at it.
   ⓒ She barked and barked at the porcupine.
   ⓓ Misty barked and barked at them.

# Subject and Object Pronouns

---

> - Use a **subject pronoun** as the subject of a sentence.
>   *I, you, he, she, it, we,* and *they* are subject pronouns.
> - Use an **object pronoun** after an action verb or after a word such as
>   *for, at, of, with,* or *to.*
>   *Me, you, him, her, it, us,* and *them* are object pronouns.

Look at the pictures. Proofread and combine sentences on the lines.

**1.** This is a box turtle. They needs its shell. Without them, the turtle cannot live.

_____

**2.** These are crickets. It chirp faster on warm days than on cool days. In Japan, children keep it as pets.

_____

_____

**3.** Do us see the ostrich? She dropped to the ground and stretched her neck because an enemy is near. Now the enemy can't see them.

_____

_____

**4.** Look at the goats. Him and her will eat just about anything. The goats will not eat tin cans, though. That is a fable. Fruits, vegetables, and grass are better for it.

_____

_____

# Possessive Pronouns

> • A **possessive pronoun** takes the place of a possessive noun. It shows who or what owns something.
> Some possessive pronouns are used before nouns (*my, your, his, her, its, our, your, their*).

Draw a line under the possessive pronouns.

1. The teacher said, "Read your book."

2. The Many Lives of Benjamin Franklin is its title.

3. Ben Franklin helped form our nation.

4. Ben Franklin spent his childhood in Boston.

5. The Franklins had seventeen children, so their family was large.

6. Do you wonder how Mrs. Franklin took care of her family?

7. Perhaps the older children helped to take care of their younger brothers and sisters.

8. Even though Ben was one of many children, his parents knew that he was special.

**8** Book 3.2/Unit 2
**Many Lives of Benjamin Franklin**

**Extension:** Ask students to write several sentences about Benjamin Franklin with possessive pronouns.

**141**

# Possessive Pronouns

---

> • Some **possessive pronouns** can stand alone (*mine, yours, his, hers, its, ours, yours, theirs*).

---

Read the sentences and the possessive pronouns in ( ). Write the correct possessive pronoun.

1. Here is _____ report on Ben Franklin.                    (my, mine)

2. Ted and I are almost finished with _____.               (our, ours)

3. Did you finish _____ yet?                               (your, yours)

4. I finished _____ the other night.                       (my, mine)

5. I wonder if James and Ann finished                           (their, theirs)
   _____ reports.

6. I think they handed _____ in already.                   (their, theirs)

7. What part of Franklin's life did you write                   (your, yours)
   about in _____ report?

8. Ann wrote about Ben Franklin's                               (her, hers)
   childhood in _____.

9. James wrote about Ben Franklin's                             (his, its)
   inventions in _____ .

10. Don't you think Ben Franklin was                            (our, ours)
    one of _____ greatest heroes?

---

**Extension:** Have students work in pairs. Ask one student to use *my* in a sentence. For example, *My report is about Franklin's work in Europe.* Ask the other student to restate the sentence using *mine.*

142

Book 3.2/Unit 2
**Many Lives of Benjamin Franklin**
10

## Possessive Pronouns

---

> - A possessive pronoun takes the place of a possessive noun. It shows who or what owns something.
>   Some possessive pronouns are used before nouns.
>
>     my        our        your        his        its        their        her
>
>   Some possessive pronouns can stand alone.
>
>     hers      mine      yours      theirs      ours      his      its

Write the correct possessive pronoun to complete each sentence.

1. As a child, Ben Franklin liked to test out _____ ideas.

2. I wonder if Ben's mother ever worried about _____ son.

3. With a son like _____, she must have worried.

4. What would _____ say if she saw you being pulled across a pond by a kite?

5. I know that _____ wouldn't be too happy with me.

6. Ben's parents decided that _____ son should become a printer.

7. They sent Ben to live with James, another son of _____.

8. Would _____ brother want you to live with him?

# Using an Apostrophe

- Add an apostrophe and an *s* to a singular noun to make it possessive.

- Add an apostrophe to make most plural nouns possessive.

- Add an apostrophe and *s* to form the possessive plural nouns that do not end in *s*.

- Possessive pronouns do not have apostrophes.

Proofread the paragraph. Make corrections. Then rewrite the paragraph correctly.

Do you think your family is big? Josiah and Abiah Franklin had 17 children. Ben was the couples tenth and youngest son. The childrens father was a hardworking man who made soap and candles. The familys home was on Milk Street in Boston. At the time, Boston was one of the colonies more thriving towns. If you visit Boston today, you will find a plaque on Milk Street that marks Ben Franklins birthplace.

_____

_____

_____

_____

_____

_____

_____

_____

_____

# Possessive Pronouns

**A.** Write **yes** if the underlined word is a possessive pronoun. Write **no** if the underlined word is not a possessive pronoun.

**1.** During most of <u>Franklin's</u> life, America was ruled by England. _____

**2.** Many people wanted freedom for <u>their</u> country. _____

**3.** Franklin was sent to England in 1757 to speak up for the <u>colonies'</u> rights. _____

**4.** He spent almost eighteen years of <u>his</u> life in England. _____

**5.** When he returned in 1775, America had not yet gained <u>its</u> independence. _____

**B.** Write **yes** if the underlined word is the correct possessive pronoun. Write **no** if the underlined word is not the correct possessive pronoun.

**6.** <u>Our</u> country was already at war with England by 1775. _____

**7.** Franklin and <u>their</u> friends talked about ways to gain freedom. _____

**8.** On July 4, 1776, Franklin and others signed <u>their</u> names to the Declaration of Independence. _____

**9.** Franklin went to France to ask the King for <u>its</u> help. _____

**10.** Independence is <u>ours</u> because of people like Franklin. _____

# Possessive Pronouns

---

- A **possessive pronoun** takes the place of a possessive noun. It shows who or what owns something.
  Some possessive pronouns are used before nouns (*my, your, his, her, its, our, your, their*).
  Some possessive pronouns can stand alone (*mine, yours, his, hers, its, ours, yours, theirs*).

---

Read each sentence. Then write each one with the correct possessive pronoun.

**1.** Who is yours favorite historical figure?

_____

**2.** My is Benjamin Franklin.

_____

**3.** I think he is one of ours greatest.

_____

**4.** Stories about him are in mine history books.

_____

**5.** Last year mine parents took me to Philadelphia.

_____

**6.** That's where Franklin, her wife, and theirs children once lived.

_____

**7.** We walked in the courtyard where theirs home once stood.

_____

**8.** We saw furniture, utensils, and plates that had been their.

_____

---

**Extension:** Have students write two original related sentences to illustrate a possessive pronoun that stands alone and a possessive pronoun that is followed by a noun.

# Pronoun-Verb Agreement

- A **present-tense verb** must agree with its **subject pronoun**.
- Add *-s* to most action verbs when you use the pronouns *he, she,* and *it*.
- Do not add *-s* to an action verb in the present tense when you use the pronouns *I, we, you,* and *they*.

Choose the correct verb to complete each sentence. Write the verb.

**1.** I (live, lives) in the town of Chewandswallow. _____

**2.** On some days it (rain, rains) soup. _____

**3.** We (bring, brings) our bowls and spoons outside with us. _____

**4.** Do you (like, likes) peanut butter and jelly? _____

**5.** She (rake, rakes) up the rolls in the yard. _____

**6.** He (pour, pours) syrup on the pancakes. _____

**7.** They (gather, gathers) up some hamburgers for lunch. _____

**8.** Sometimes it (drizzle, drizzles) soda. _____

**9.** He (sneeze, sneezes) from all the pepper in the wind. _____

**10.** Today we (sail, sails) for a new land. _____

10  Book 3.2/Unit 2
**Cloudy with a Chance of Meatballs**

**Extension:** Have students identify and list action verbs from the story and then make up sentences in the present tense using the verbs and pronouns.

**147**

# The Verbs *Have* and *Be*

---

- The verbs *have* and *be* have special forms.

  | The forms of *have* | The forms of *be* |
  |---|---|
  | Use *have* with *I, you, we, they* | Use *am* with *I* |
  | Use *has* with *he, she, it* | Use *are* with *you, we, they* |
  | | Use *is* with *he, she, it* |

---

Write the correct form of the verb in ( ) to complete each sentence.

**1.** I _____ interested in books with unusual stories.　　(be)

**2.** I _____ a new book for my sister and brother.　　(have)

**3.** She _____ lots of books.　　(have)

**4.** He _____ always glad to get another new book.　　(be)

**5.** We _____ fun reading the new book.　　(have)

**6.** It _____ a story about a town called Chewandswallow.　　(be)

**7.** They _____ very unusual weather in Chewandswallow.　　(have)

**8.** Do you _____ pancake storms and maple syrup floods?　　(have)

**9.** _____ it ever cloudy with a chance of soup or meatballs?　(be)

**10.** Sometimes it _____ windy with gusts of pepper!　　(be)

**11.** We _____ glad not to have weather like that!　　(be)

**12.** We _____ rain or snow, not soup or mashed potatoes.　　(have)

---

**148**

Extension: Have students use the forms of *be* and *have* to write sentences that describe the weather.

Book 3.2/Unit 2
**Cloudy with a Chance of Meatballs**
12

# Pronoun-Verb Agreement

- A present-tense verb must agree with its subject pronoun.
- Add -*s* to most action verbs when you use the pronouns *he, she*, and *it*.
- Do not add -*s* to an action verb in the present tense when you use the pronouns *I, we, you*, and *they*.
- The verbs *have* and *be* have special forms.

| The forms of *have* | The forms of *be* |
|---|---|
| Use *have* with *I, you, we, they* | Use *am* with *I* |
| Use *has* with *he, she, it* | Use *are* with *you, we, they* |
| | Use *is* with *he, she, it* |

Write a pronoun to complete the answer to each question.

**1.** Look outside. What is the weather like right now?

_____ is sunny and warm.

**2.** What does the weather reporter predict?

_____ predicts rain.

**3.** What kind of weather do the people of Chewandswallow have?

_____ have strange weather.

**4.** What does it drizzle in Chewandswallow at times?

_____ drizzles soda.

**5.** What does Grandpa have for flipping pancakes?

_____ has a pancake flipper.

**6.** Are you hungry for a plate of pancakes with syrup?

_____ am not hungry for pancakes.

**7.** What are Chewandswallow streets like after a shower?

_____ are sticky.

**8.** Where do you put leftovers after a big meal?

_____ put leftovers in the refrigerator.

Book 3.2/Unit 2
**Cloudy with a Chance of Meatballs**
8

**Extension:** Ask students to write three questions that include an action verb, a form of *have*, and a form of *be*. Then tell children to trade papers and answer the questions.

149

# Using Capital Letters and Commas

> - A proper noun begins with a capital letter.
> - The name of a day, month, or holiday begins with a capital letter.
> - Use a comma between the names of a city and a state.
> - Use a comma between the day and year in a date.

Read the paragraph. Make corrections. Write the paragraph.

We are from the tiny town of greendale New york. It is a very old town. On may 21 2002, greendale turns 250 years old. It has a main Street with stores, houses with trees and gardens, a schoolhouse, and about three hundred people. greendale has food stores It also has sunny days, snowy days, rainy days, and cloudy days. On thanksgiving day, greendale celebrates with free turkey dinners.

_____

_____

_____

_____

_____

_____

_____

_____

_____

# Pronoun-Verb Agreement

**A.** Read each group of sentences. Mark the one with the subject pronoun and action verb that do not agree.

1. ⓐ They enjoy pancakes every Saturday morning.
   ⓑ He makes them for Henry, his sister, and their mom.
   ⓒ It takes him about a half hour in all.
   ⓓ They eats them in half that time.

2. ⓐ I like pancakes with syrup.
   ⓑ We help my mother.
   ⓒ You stirs together some flour, milk, and eggs.
   ⓓ Then you put them on a hot griddle.

**B.** Read the sentences. Choose the correct verb form to complete each sentence. Mark your answer.

3. I _____ from Chewandswallow.
   ⓐ am
   ⓑ have
   ⓒ is
   ⓓ are

4. We _____ no food stores.
   ⓐ has
   ⓑ are
   ⓒ am
   ⓓ have

5. They _____ not necessary.
   ⓐ have
   ⓑ is
   ⓒ are
   ⓓ am

# Pronoun-Verb Agreement

- A present-tense verb must agree with its subject pronoun.
- Add -s to most action verbs when you use the pronouns *he, she,* and *it.*
- Do not add -s to an action verb in the present tense when you use *I, we, you,* and *they.*
- The verbs *have* and *be* have special forms.

**Mechanics**

- A proper noun begins with a capital letter.
- The name of a day, month, or holiday begins with a capital letter.

Read each sentence aloud. Change the verbs to make them agree with the subject pronouns. Put capital letters where they belong. Write the sentences.

**1.** They sure has strange weather in chewandswallow.

_____

**2.** Sometimes it snow mashed potatoes or peas.

_____

**3.** It are monday and almost time for lunch.

_____

**4.** I is on main street with henry and his sister.

_____

**5.** He want pork chops and salad.

_____

**6.** She hope for soup.

_____

# Contractions with Pronouns

---

- A **contraction** is a shortened form of two words.

| | | |
|---|---|---|
| I am = I'm | we are = we're | he has = he's |
| he is = he's | you are = you're | she has = she's |
| she is = she's | they are = they're | it has = it's |
| it is = it's | | |

---

Replace the underlined words with a contraction. Then write each sentence.

**1.** <u>We are</u> learning about fossil fuels.

_____

**2.** <u>You are</u> not going to believe this.

_____

**3.** <u>They are</u> formed over millions of years.

_____

**4.** <u>It is</u> important to find new kinds of clean energy.

_____

**5.** <u>I am</u> sending for a book on sun and wind power.

_____

**6.** Our teacher says <u>she has</u> got a film on solar energy.

_____

**7.** <u>She is</u> also taking us to a windmill farm.

_____

**8.** My dad says <u>he has</u> seen a solar-powered car model!

_____

---

**Extension:** Write the following on the board: What is __? What are __? Who will __? Who has __? Where is __? Have students make up questions and take turns answering them using contractions with pronouns.

153

# More Contractions with Pronouns

> • Remember, a **contraction** is a shortened form of two words. Here are more contractions.
>
> | | | |
> |---|---|---|
> | I have = I've | I will = I'll | we will = we'll |
> | you have = you've | he will = he'll | you will = you'll |
> | we have = we've | she will = she'll | they will = they'll |
> | they have = they've | | |

Underline the two words in each sentence that you can make into a contraction. Then write each sentence with the contraction.

**1.** One day we will run out of fossil fuels.

_____

**2.** It will be five billion years before the sun burns out.

_____

**3.** We have got to find ways to better use the wind and sun.

_____

**4.** You will be amazed by the possibilities.

_____

**5.** You have probably heard of windmill and solar farms.

_____

**6.** I have seen them in California.

_____

**7.** One day I will build a house with solar panels.

_____

**8.** They will catch sunlight and turn it into electricity.

_____

154
**Extension:** Have students write questions using pronouns and then take turns answering them, using contractions with pronouns in their answers.

Book 3.2/Unit 2
**Pure Power**
8

Name_____ Date_____

# Contractions with Pronouns

---

- A **contraction** is a shortened form of two words.

| | | |
|---|---|---|
| I am = I'm | I have = I've | I will = I'll |
| he is = he's | you have = you've | he will = he'll |
| she is = she's | we have = we've | she will = she'll |
| it is = it's | they have = they've | it will = it'll |
| we are = we're | he has = he's | we will = we'll |
| you are = you're | she has = she's | you will = you'll |
| they are = they're | it has = it's | they will = they'll |

---

Complete each sentence with a contraction that makes sense.

I. _____ hearing more about wind power all the time.

2. _____ been using windmills for centuries in the Netherlands.

3. Now _____ popping up in the United States, Asia, and Europe.

4. _____ been to a windmill farm in California.

5. _____ really awesome to see 6,500 windmills in one place.

6. _____ got to see it to believe it.

7. _____ absolutely amaze you.

8. Perhaps _____ use electricity generated by windmills one day.

9. Maybe _____ already using electricity generated by windmills.

10. In the future, _____ probably use more solar energy as well.

---

# Using an Apostrophe

---

> • An **apostrophe** takes the place of letters.
>
> • Possessive pronouns do not have apostrophes.
>
> • Do not confuse possessive pronouns with contractions.

Read the paragraph. Make the corrections. Then write the paragraph correctly on the lines below.

its vital to find better sources of energy. Their saying that energy from fossil fuels is the biggest cause of pollution. Weve been seeing the terrible effects on our planet for a long time. today were looking to the sun and the wind for answers to our energy problems. Scientists around the world are working together. Im sure theyll find efficient ways to turn sunlight and wind into electricity.

_____

_____

_____

_____

_____

_____

_____

_____

_____

# Contractions with Pronouns

**A.** Is the underlined contraction correctly written? Write **yes** if it is. Write **no** if it is not.

1. <u>Were</u> running out of oil and coal. _____

2. When <u>they're</u> burned, they cause pollution. _____

3. <u>Its'</u> clean energy. _____

4. <u>I'ave</u> got a great idea! _____

5. <u>I'm</u> going to build a house with solar panels on the roof. _____

**B.** Write the contraction for the underlined words.

6. <u>You are</u> not going to believe it. _____

7. <u>They have</u> built a windmill "farm." _____

8. <u>It has</u> been running for a year. _____

9. <u>You will</u> likely see them in many places before long. _____

10. <u>We have</u> got to find ways to prevent pollution. _____

# Contractions with Pronouns

---

• A **contraction** is a shortened form of two words.

---

**Mechanics**

• An apostrophe takes the place of letters.

• Possessive pronouns do not have apostrophes.

• Do not confuse possessive pronouns with contractions.

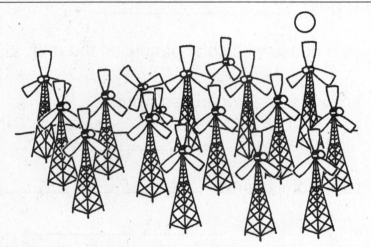

Look at the picture. Read the sentences. Write the sentences correctly.

1. Its a picture of windmills at a windmill farm.

   _____

2. Theyve got light blades.

   _____

3. Their able to catch more wind than ever before.

   _____

4. Itll turn the wind into electricity.

   _____

5. Theyll help make Earth clean.

   _____

# Pronouns

Read each passage. Choose a word or group or words that belong in each space. Mark your answer.

Ann read <u>Lon Po Po</u> to James and __(1)__. She says the story is a folk tale. Have you heard the tale before? Ann says <u>Lon Po Po</u> reminds her of <u>Little Red Riding Hood</u>. __(2)__ agree with her.

**1.** ⓐ I
ⓑ me
ⓒ we
ⓓ us

**2.** ⓔ I
ⓕ me
ⓖ us
ⓗ she

One day, my parents brought me to a museum. They taught me how to look at paintings. Today, when I see __(3)__ I feel happy. I love paintings of flowers and landscapes. __(4)__ make me dream of beautiful places.

**3.** ⓐ they
ⓑ them
ⓒ their
ⓓ theirs

**4.** ⓔ They
ⓕ Them
ⓖ Their
ⓗ Theirs

She sat beside a boy in the concert last night. The boy was blind. __(5)__ liked the music very much. The songs were his favorites. __(6)__ applause was always loud and long. The musicians were grateful.

**5.** ⓐ He
ⓑ His
ⓒ Him
ⓓ He's

**6.** ⓔ He
ⓕ His
ⓖ Him
ⓗ He's

I like pancakes with syrup. You __(7)__ together some flour, milk, and eggs. Then you put them in a griddle. They __(8)__ good!

**7.** ⓐ stir
ⓑ stirs
ⓒ does
ⓓ do

**8.** ⓔ am
ⓕ is
ⓖ are
ⓗ be

Have you gone to a shoe store by yourself? I __(9)__ done it. It is quite an experience. You go to the shelves and look at the display. You get what you like and fit the shoes. You pay the cashier and they're __(10)__.

**9.** ⓐ has
ⓑ have
ⓒ is
ⓓ am

**10.** ⓔ your
ⓕ yours
ⓖ you're
ⓗ you'll

It will be five billion years before the sun burns out. __(11)__ got to find better ways to use the wind and sun. One day __(12)__ build a house with solar panels.

**11.** ⓐ We'd
ⓑ We've
ⓒ We'll
ⓓ We're

**12.** ⓔ I'll
ⓕ I've
ⓖ I'm
ⓗ I's

# Adjectives

---

- An **adjective** is a word that describes a noun.

- An adjective tells **what kind** or **how many**.
  What kind: Papa was in a <u>bad</u> mood.
  How many: <u>Many</u> fans are sitting in the bleachers.

Draw a line under each adjective. Draw two lines under the noun that the adjective describes.

1. Reginald hears metal cleats stomp on the floor.

2. He hears Papa's loud voice.

3. Reginald brings Mr. Forrest six bats.

4. Papa tells Reginald to carry one bat at a time.

5. Mr. Forrest misses the ball three times.

6. Reginald looks at Papa's crinkled face.

7. Mr. LaRue hits a home run and touches four bases.

8. Then several players get hits.

9. Papa makes an important announcement.

10. The Dukes and the Monarchs play on a sunny day.

---

**10** Book 3.2/Unit 3
**The Bat Boy and His Violin**

**Extension:** Have students write a list of adjectives to describe a musical instrument. Then have them use one of the adjectives to write a sentence about the instrument.

**161**

# Articles

> - The words *a, an,* and *the* are special adjectives called **articles**.
> - Use *a* and *an* before singular nouns. Use *a* before a word starting with a consonant and *an* before a word starting with a vowel.
> - Use *the* before a singular or plural noun.

Complete each sentence with the correct article in parentheses.

1. Reginald plays _____ violin. (an, the)

2. He will have _____ recital next month. (a, an)

3. Papa is _____ manager of the Dukes. (an, the)

4. The Dukes need _____ batboy. (a, an)

5. In Cleveland, _____ bleachers are packed with fans. (an, the)

6. Reginald drops _____ bats. (an, the)

7. One bat almost hits _____ umpire's head. (a, an)

8. Reginald hears _____ fans howl. (an, the)

9. Mr. Forrest gets _____ out. (a, an)

10. The last game is _____ important game. (a, an)

162

**Extension:** Have students look for the articles a, an, and the on several pages of their science or social studies books and count the number of times these words appear.

Book 3.2/Unit 3
The Bat Boy and His Violin
10

# Adjectives That Tell *What Kind* or *How Many*

- An **adjective** tells **what kind** or **how many**.
- Use the articles *a* and *an* before singular nouns. Use *a* before a word starting with a consonant and *an* before a word starting with a vowel.
- Use *the* before a singular or plural noun.

Complete each sentence with an adjective from the box.

| a | an | the | few | one | quiet | rickety | lovely |
|---|----|-----|-----|-----|-------|---------|--------|

**1.** The team rides on _____ old bus.

**2.** It is a _____ bus.

**3.** For three weeks, _____ team wins all its games.

**4.** Then the Dukes lose to the Monarchs by _____ run.

**5.** On the _____ ride home, Reginald plays the violin.

**6.** A _____ weeks later, Reginald performs a recital.

**7.** He plays a _____ tune on his violin.

**8.** Reginald is _____ talented boy.

## Correcting Sentences

> • Use **commas** to separate three or more words in a series.
> The musical instruments are big, loud, and heavy.

Proofread the sentences. Add commas where they belong.

1. The baseball players are big strong and fast.

2. Three players stand at first second and third bases.

3. Other players stand in left field center field and right field.

4. A team also has a pitcher a catcher and a shortstop.

5. The pitcher may throw a fastball a curve ball or a slider.

6. An umpire calls the strikes balls and outs.

7. A batter may get a hit a walk or an out.

8. Mosley LaRue and Ervin are on the baseball team.

9. The batboy plays Beethoven Mozart and Bach on his violin.

10. After the game, the players are tired disappointed and quiet.

**Extension:** Have students work in pairs. Ask each student to write a
sentence, with three or more words in a series, about a sport. Then
have partners exchange sentences and put in commas where needed.

164

Book 3.2/Unit 3
**The Bat Boy and His Violin**

10

# Adjectives

Find the adjective that tells what kind or how many. Write the adjective on the line.

**1.** It is a tough season for Papa. _____

**2.** He has lost many players. _____

**3.** Reginald lines up the shiny bats. _____

**4.** The team gets two outs quickly. _____

**5.** After nine innings, the Dukes win the game. _____

Decide if *a, an,* or *the* belongs in the sentence. Write your answer on the line.

**6.** The violin is _____ kind of musical instrument.

**7.** Reginald moves a bow across _____ strings.

**8.** He hopes to play in _____ orchestra someday.

# Adjectives

---

- An **adjective** tells **what kind** or **how many**.
- Use the articles *a* and *an* before singular nouns. Use *a* before a word starting with a consonant and *an* before a word starting with a vowel.
- Use *the* before a singular or plural noun.

---

**Mechanics:**
- Use commas to separate three or more words in a series.

---

Correct each underlined article. Put commas where they belong.
Then write the sentences correctly.

1. The baseball player has a brown mitt <u>an</u> white hat and black shoes.

_____

2. <u>A</u> olive green fence stands on the green lush and beautiful grass.

_____

3. On <u>a</u> orange wooden scoreboard are the numbers of runs hits and errors.

_____

_____

4. <u>A</u> final score is 18–17. _____

Now use the sentences to color and complete the picture above.

---

# Adjectives That Compare

---

- Add *-er* to an adjective to compare two nouns.
- Add *-est* to an adjective to compare more than two nouns.
  An ant is <u>smaller</u> than a cricket.
  The <u>warmest</u> sections of an ant's nest are the bottom sections.

---

Circle the correct adjective for each sentence.

**1.** The crystal was the (sweeter, sweetest) food the queen had ever tasted.

**2.** The beginning of the ants' journey is (longer, longest) than the end.

**3.** Night is (darker, darkest) than dusk.

**4.** The brown lake was (hotter, hottest) than the water.

**5.** A blue-green firefly is (brighter, brightest) than a black ant.

**6.** The bad ants are the (smaller, smallest) things in the chamber.

**7.** The chamber makes the (louder, loudest) sounds the ants had ever heard.

**8.** The tired ants are the (slower, slowest) ants in the line.

---

8 Book 3.2/Unit 3
**Two Bad Ants**

**Extension:** Have students write a sentence comparing two nouns and another sentence comparing more than two nouns.

**167**

# Adjectives That Compare

> - In adjectives ending in a consonant and *y*, change the *y* to *i* and add -*er* or -*est*.
>
> - In adjectives ending in *e*, drop the *e* and add -*er* or -*est*.
>
> - In adjectives that have a single vowel before a final consonant, double the final consonant and add -*er* or -*est*.
>
>   | Change *y* to *i*: | happy | happier | happiest |
>   | --- | --- | --- | --- |
>   | Drop the *e*: | safe | safer | safest |
>   | Double the consonant: | hot | hotter | hottest |

Add -*er* or -*est* to each adjective. Write the correct form.

**Add** -*er*.

1. pretty _____
2. blue _____
3. big _____
4. noisy _____
5. red _____

**Add** -*est*.

6. white _____
7. tiny _____
8. pale _____
9. fat _____
10. silly _____

Write the correct form of each adjective in parentheses.

11. A sugar crystal is (tasty) _____ than a bread crumb.

12. The leaves with dew are (wet) _____ than the ones with no dew.

13. Worker ants are the (busy) _____ ants in the colony.

14. The house was the (strange) _____ place the ants had ever seen.

15. In the end, the bad ants are the (happy) _____ ants of all.

**Extension:** Ask students to choose one of the adjectives from the -*er* or -*est* lists and then use the word to draw a picture in which they compare two or three things.

168

Book 3.2/Unit 3
**Two Bad Ants**

15

# Adjectives That Compare

- Add *-er* to an adjective to compare two nouns and *-est* to compare more than two nouns.
- In adjectives ending in a consonant and *y*, first change the *y* to *i*.
- In adjectives ending in *e*, first drop the *e*.
- In adjectives that have a single vowel before a final consonant, first double the final consonant.

Rewrite each sentence. Use the correct form of the underlined adjective.

**1.** The journey was the <u>long</u> journey the ants had ever taken.

_____

**2.** The ant scout seemed to be the <u>fast</u> ant of all.

_____

**3.** Sounds of hungry spiders were <u>scary</u> than crickets calling.

_____

**4.** Going home was <u>wise</u> than staying behind.

_____

**5.** The disk with holes was <u>hot</u> than the brown lake.

_____

**6.** The house was the <u>odd</u> place the ants had ever seen.

_____

**7.** Their home was the <u>safe</u> place in the world for the bad ants.

_____

**8.** The ant queen was among the <u>happy</u> ants in the nest.

_____

**Extension:** Invite students to choose two or three classroom objects and compare them in sentences using adjectives that compare.

# Correcting Sentences

- Use quotation marks at the beginning and end of a person's exact words.
- Use a comma after the name of a person spoken to.
- Use a comma after the words *yes* and *no* when they begin a sentence.

Proofread the sentences. Correct adjectives that are misspelled. Add quotation marks and commas where they belong. Then write the sentences correctly.

**1.** The story about the bad ants is the funnyest story I ever read, said Josh.

_____

_____

**2.** I think the ant scout was the braviest of all the ants, added Maria.

_____

**3.** Josh is the ant scout biger than the ant queen? asked Suzy.

_____

**4.** No the ant queen is the largst ant in the colony, Josh answered.

_____

**5.** The bad ants were smartter on the second day than on the first day, said Derek.

_____

_____

**Extension:** Have students write a sentence with a person's exact words. Have them write another sentence beginning with the name of a person. Then have them write a third sentence beginning with the word *yes* or *no*.

170

Book 3.2/Unit 3
**Two Bad Ants**
5

# Adjectives That Compare

Read each sentence. Find the sentence that has an adjective that compares. Mark your answer.

1. ⓐ The ants march into the dark woods.
   ⓑ Woods are darker than meadows.
   ⓒ Some ants are red and black.
   ⓓ There are many tunnels in an ant nest.

2. ⓐ Worker ants are busy ants.
   ⓑ The ant queen is a hungry ant.
   ⓒ The scout is an important ant.
   ⓓ Two bad ants are the silliest ants of all.

3. ⓐ Giant waves fall over the ants.
   ⓑ A toaster has a red glow.
   ⓒ A spoon is bigger than an ant.
   ⓓ The ants see a shiny fountain.

Read each sentence. Find the correct form of the adjective in parentheses.

4. A flea is (tiny) than an ant.
   ⓐ tinyer
   ⓑ tinier
   ⓒ tiniest
   ⓓ tiner

5. A grasshopper is (long) than an ant.
   ⓐ longer
   ⓑ longeer
   ⓒ longier
   ⓓ longest

## Adjectives That Compare

> • Add *-er* to an adjective to compare two nouns and *-est* to compare more than two nouns.

> **Mechanics:**
>
> • Use quotation marks at the beginning and end of a person's exact words.
>
> • Use a comma after the name of a person spoken to.
>
> • Use a comma after the words *yes* and *no* when they begin a sentence.

Listen as your partner reads each sentence aloud. Rewrite the sentences. Correct the underlined adjectives. Put quotation marks and commas where they belong.

1. The path in the forest was <u>longest</u> than the tunnel, said Mark.

_____

2. Lou are ants <u>blackest</u> than night? asked Tara.

_____

3. To ants, the house seemed <u>highest</u> than a mountain, said Mark.

_____

4. Yes the house was the <u>stranger</u> place the ants had ever seen, said Lou.

_____

_____

5. The ants thought the crystals were the <u>brighter</u> crystals in the world, said Tara.

_____

_____

Read the new sentences to your partner. Do they make sense?

# Adverbs

> - An **adverb** is a word that tells more about a verb.
>
> - Some adverbs tell **how** an action takes place.
>
> - Most adverbs that tell how end in *-ly.* They are formed by adding *-ly* to an adjective.
>   A salmon swims *swiftly.*

Draw a line under each adverb that tells how. Draw two lines under the verb it describes.

1. Many dogs eagerly perform tricks.

2. A sheepdog herds sheep easily.

3. Suddenly, one sheep leaves the flock.

4. Immediately, the dog decides what to do.

5. Sheepdogs seem to carefully plan their actions.

6. A sheepdog moves quickly.

7. Other animals work slowly.

8. A lion quietly watches its prey.

9. Parrots squawk loudly.

10. Other birds sing sweetly.

**Extension:** Have students complete these sentences with adverbs that tell how: We speak _____. They listen _____. He plays _____. She runs _____.

# Adverbs

---

- Adverbs can be put in different places in a sentence. Moving an adverb may make the sentence sound better.
  Sheepdogs seem to *plan carefully* their actions.
  Sheepdogs seem to *carefully plan* their actions.

---

Add **ly** to the adjective in parentheses to form an adverb. Write the sentence, placing the adverb where you think it sounds best.

**1.** (deep) Whales dive.

_____

**2.** (smooth) A dolphin swims.

_____

**3.** (immediate) Beavers repair a broken dam.

_____

**4.** (curious) Chimps look at things.

_____

**5.** (correct) Alex, the parrot, counts.

_____

**6.** (sound) Bears sleep during the winter.

_____

**7.** (fierce) Some animals fight each other.

_____

**8.** (close) Scientists are studying animals.

_____

**Extension:** Ask students to rewrite sentences 1-3, using different adverbs.

Book 3.2/Unit 3
**Do Animals Think?** 8

# Adverbs That Tell *How*

- An **adverb** is a word that tells more about a verb.

- Most adverbs that tell **how** end in *-ly*. They are formed by adding *-ly* to an adjective.

- Adverbs can be put in different places in a sentence.

Circle each adverb. Then use the adverbs to complete the sentences. Place each adverb where you think it sounds best.

| carefully | fly | gracefully | hilly | noisily | suddenly | valley | wildly |

**I.** During a storm, the wind blows.

_____

**2.** The wind may destroy a spider's web.

_____

**3.** A spider will spin another web.

_____

**4.** A panther moves.

_____

**5.** A crow calls.

_____

⑤ Book 3.2/Unit 3
**Do Animals Think?**

**Extension:** Invite students to use each of the adverbs in sentences of their own.

175

## Correcting a Paragraph

- Use a capital letter to begin the first word and each important word in a title.

- Underline the title of a book.

Proofread the paragraph. Check to see whether adverbs are used correctly. Also check to see that the book titles are written correctly. Then rewrite the paragraph on the lines below.

> I like to read about animals. Scientists feel that some animals may actual think. When I go to the library, I usual look for books about animals. First I looked at the pictures quick. Then I read the story careful. One of my favorite books is Two bad ants. I also like the book dream Wolf.

_____

_____

_____

_____

_____

_____

_____

_____

_____

_____

**Extension:** Invite students to find and share examples of
book titles from the classroom library. Have students
point out the words that begin with capital letters.

**176**

Book 3.2/Unit 3
**Do Animals Think?** 10

## Adverbs That Tell *How*

Change the adjective in parentheses to an adverb. Write the adverb on the line.

**1.** Some animals (actual) _____ solve problems.

**2.** Chimps figure out things (quick) _____ .

**3.** Other animals do things (different) _____ .

**4.** Cows move (slow) _____ .

**5.** Rabbits run away (rapid) _____ .

Underline each adverb. Write **yes** if the adverb is in the best place. Write **no** if it is not in the best place.

**6.** A scientist introduces proudly Alex. _____

**7.** Suddenly, Alex starts talking. _____

**8.** Alex names objects easily. _____

**9.** The audience wildly claps. _____

**10.** Alex flaps his wings excitedly. _____

# Adverbs That Tell *How*

---

- An **adverb** is a word that tells more about a verb.

- Most adverbs that tell **how** end in *-ly*. They are formed by adding *-ly* to an adjective.

**Mechanics:**

- Use a capital letter to begin the first word and each important word in a title.

- Underline the title of a book.

Read the sentences. Correct each underlined adverb. Circle each letter that should be a capital letter. Draw a line under each book title.

**1.** Hana is reading a book called chimps and tools.

**2.** She learns that chimps use tools <u>easy</u>. _____

**3.** The title of Deacon's book is a wolf's story.

**4.** Sometimes a wolf will howl <u>loud</u>. _____

**5.** Both children are reading <u>quiet</u>. _____

Write the title of one of your favorite books.

_____

# Adverbs That Tell *When*

---

- Some adverbs tell **when** an action takes place.
- Adverbs that tell when include *first, always, next, after, tomorrow, soon, early, today, then, yesterday*.

---

Draw a line under each adverb that tells when. Draw two lines under the verb it describes.

1. Charlotte rebuilds her web today.

2. Yesterday, an insect made a hole in Charlotte's web.

3. Charlotte noticed the hole early this morning.

4. Fern always watches Charlotte.

5. She will watch Charlotte tomorrow.

6. Soon Wilbur decides to spin a web.

7. First Wilbur breathes deeply.

8. Then he climbs on a manure pile.

9. Wilbur jumps into the air next.

10. He soon finds himself on the ground.

---

10 Book 3.2/Unit 3
**Charlotte's Web**

**Extension:** Encourage students to brainstorm as
many other adverbs as they can that tell when.

**179**

# Adverbs That Tell *Where*

---

- Some adverbs tell **where** an action takes place.
- Adverbs that tell where include *there, outside, up, here, nearby, ahead, around, far, away, everywhere.*

Draw a line under each adverb that tells where. Draw two lines under the verb it describes.

1. Wilbur stood in the doorway and looked up.

2. He knew his friend was here in the barn.

3. Wilbur saw Charlotte there in her web.

4. As he jumped, Wilbur looked around for his dragline.

5. Then Wilbur walked outside.

6. Templeton, a rat, was nearby.

7. He sat just ahead under the trough.

8. Templeton went away for a minute.

9. His hole under the trough was not far.

10. There Templeton found a piece of string.

**Extension:** Ask students to brainstorm as many other adverbs as they can that tell where.

Book 3.2/Unit 3
**Charlotte's Web**    /10

# Adverbs That Tell *Where* and *When*

> - Some adverbs tell **when** an action takes place.
> - Some adverbs tell **where** an action takes place.

Circle the adverb in each sentence. Write **when** if the adverb tells when. Write **where** if the adverb tells where.

1. Our class is visiting a farm tomorrow. _____

2. The bus is leaving early. _____

3. First we'll go to the barn. _____

4. Maybe we will see a spider there. _____

5. We can look up in the corners. _____

6. We will also look at the animals outside. _____

7. I want to look around for a pig's trough. _____

8. I always like to see farm animals. _____

**Extension:** Have students choose a magazine picture and write a description of the picture. Ask students to use at least two adverbs that tell when and two adverbs that tell where.

# Correcting Sentences

> - Every sentence begins with a capital letter.
> - A statement ends with a period.
> - A question ends with a question mark.
> - A command ends with a period.
> - An exclamation ends with an exclamation point.

Write each sentence. Fill in an adverb from the box. Add capital letters and the correct end marks.

| nearby | late | first | always |
|--------|------|-------|--------|

**1.** do you know what _____ happens to Charlotte's web

_____

**2.** insects _____ put holes in her web

_____

**3.** it's _____ in the day when Charlotte does her weaving

_____

**4.** standing _____, Wilbur talks to Charlotte

_____

**5.** what does Charlotte want Wilbur to do _____

_____

**6.** _____, take a deep breath

_____

**Extension:** Have students look in newspapers to find examples of statements, commands, questions, and exclamations. Ask students to underline the examples.

# When or Where

Choose the word in each sentence that is an adverb.

**1.** Fern sat nearby and listened to the conversation.
- ⓐ sat
- ⓑ nearby
- ⓒ listened
- ⓓ conversation

**2.** Today Fern saw an interesting event.
- ⓐ Today
- ⓑ saw
- ⓒ interesting
- ⓓ event

Decide which word in the sentence is an adverb that tells **when**. Mark your answer.

**3.** First Wilbur went outside to find a piece of string.
- ⓐ First
- ⓑ went
- ⓒ outside
- ⓓ find

**4.** Templeton looked around and soon found some string.
- ⓐ looked
- ⓑ around
- ⓒ soon
- ⓓ found

Decide which word in the sentence is an adverb that tells **where**. Mark your answer.

**5.** Then Wilbur walked away with a string on his tail.
- ⓐ Then
- ⓑ walked
- ⓒ away
- ⓓ with

**6.** Next Wilbur jumped down from the manure pile again.
- ⓐ Next
- ⓑ jumped
- ⓒ down
- ⓓ from

# *When* or *Where*

---

> • Some adverbs tell **when** an action takes place.
>
> • Some adverbs tell **where** an action takes place.

---

**Mechanics:**

• Every sentence begins with a capital letter.

• A statement ends with a period.

• A question ends with a question mark.

• A command ends with a period.

• An exclamation ends with an exclamation point.

---

Work with a partner. One of you reads the sentences aloud. The other proofreads. Correct the underlined adverbs. Put capital letters and end marks where they belong. The proofreader reads the corrected sentences aloud.

**1.** the rat was sitting <u>out</u> the barn

**2.** he looked <u>ups</u> at Wilbur

**3.** <u>ten</u> Wilbur asked for a piece of string

**4.** did Templeton have to go <u>fair</u>

**5.** what a great pig Wilbur was

---

# Sentence Combining with Adjectives and Adverbs

> • Two sentences can be combined by adding an **adjective** to one sentence.
> Rescuers are moving koalas. The rescuers are careful.
> <u>Careful</u> rescuers are moving koalas.

Add an adjective to combine each pair of sentences. Write the new sentences.

**1.** Rescuers are saving animals.
The animals are furry.

_____

**2.** Koalas have claws.
The claws are sharp.

_____

**3.** Koalas are animals.
They are wild.

_____

**4.** Koalas make a noise.
It's a funny noise.

_____

**5.** Koalas live in trees.
The trees are tall.

_____

**Extension:** Have students write two sentences about the same animal. Then have students combine the sentences by adding an adjective.

# Sentence Combining with Adjectives and Adverbs

---

- Two sentences can be combined by adding an **adverb** to one sentence.

  A rope loops around a koala's neck. It loops gently.

  A rope <u>gently</u> loops around a koala's neck.

Add an adverb to combine each pair of sentences. Write the new sentences.

**1.** A koala eats.
She eats quietly.

_____

**2.** Rescuers move koalas.
They move them safely.

_____

**3.** Koalas are put in crates.
They are put in carefully.

_____

**4.** The koala walked.
She walked away.

_____

**5.** Five koalas get in line.
They get in line slowly.

_____

---

**Extension:** Have students write two sentences that tell about the same action. Then have students combine the sentences by adding an adverb that tells where, when, or how.

Book 3.2/Unit 3
**The Koala Catchers**  /5

# Sentence Combining with Adjectives and Adverbs

- Two sentences can be combined by adding an **adjective** to one sentence.

- Two sentences can be combined by adding an **adverb** to one sentence.

Read each pair of sentences. Combine each pair by adding an adjective or an adverb.

**1.** People look at the koala.
They look up.

_____

**2.** The people see a koala.
She is sleepy.

_____

**3.** The koala hears flapping.
She hears it suddenly.

_____

**4.** Many koalas have a new home.
The home is safe.

_____

**5.** The photo shows koalas.
The koalas are cute.

_____

**Extension:** Have partners write two other pairs of sentences about koalas. Tell students to include an adjective in one pair and an adverb in the other pair, then combine each pair into one sentence.

# Correcting a Letter

- Begin the greeting and closing in a letter with a capital letter.
- Use a comma after the greeting in a letter.
- Use a comma after the closing in a letter.

Proofread the postcard. Add commas where they belong. Circle letters that should be capital letters. Find the sentences that can be combined by adding an adjective or adverb. Then write the postcard correctly.

dear lee

    I just read about koalas. A koala looks like a bear. Koalas are furry. They have big noses. The noses are black. people are moving koalas. Their new homes have more leaves for them to eat.

                   your friend

                   jackie

_____

_____

_____

_____

            _____

            _____

**Extension:** Invite students to write a postcard of their own and tell someone about koalas.

Book 3.2/Unit 3
**The Koala Catchers** 8

# Sentence Combining with Adjectives and Adverbs

Write the adjective that can be used to combine each pair of
sentences.

1. Many animals live in Australia.
   The animals are unusual. _____

2. There are large kangaroos in Australia.
   The kangaroos are red. _____

3. Crocodiles live in Australia's northern swamps.
   They are fierce. _____

Write the adverb that can be used to combine each pair of sentences.

4. The dingo of Australia howls.
   It howls sadly. _____

5. The wombat digs a burrow.
   The wombat easily digs. _____

# Sentence Combining with Adjectives and Adverbs

- Two sentences can be combined by adding an **adjective** to one sentence.

- Two sentences can be combined by adding an **adverb** to one sentence.

**Mechanics:**

- Begin the greeting and closing in a letter with a capital letter.
- Use a comma after the greeting in a letter.
- Use a comma after the closing in a letter.

Read the letter. Put commas where they belong. Draw three lines under letters that should be capital letters. On the lines below, write each pair of underlined sentences as one sentence. Add an adjective or an adverb.

dear karla

　　Here's a picture I drew of a koala. I think a koala is cute. <u>A koala has ears. The ears are big.</u> I hope you like my drawing. <u>Koalas can climb trees. They can climb easily.</u>

　　　　　　　　your friend

　　　　　　　　james

_____

_____

## Adjectives and Adverbs

Read the passage and look at the underlined parts. Is there a better way to say each part? If there is, which is the better way? Mark your answer.

The lake is a pretty spot for a story. I know an old legend about it. <u>Long ago, a lady came to this lake.</u> She was a good queen who took care of her people. They say that until now, she has lived in the lake. <u>Sometimes, she appears during a moon.</u>
(1)
(2)

1. ⓐ Long ago, a beautiful lady came to this lake.
   ⓑ Long ago, came to this big lake.
   ⓒ Long ago, lady on the lake.
   ⓓ No mistake.

2. ⓔ Sometimes, she appears a moon.
   ⓕ Sometimes, a full moon appears as she.
   ⓖ Sometimes, she appears during a full moon.
   ⓗ No mistake.

Every animal is interesting. <u>A wolf is smart than a spider.</u> An ant is busier than an elephant. A polar bear is whiter than a sheep. <u>Among a cow, dog, and squirrel, a cow has the big brain.</u>
(3)
(4)

3. ⓐ A wolf is smartest than a spider.
   ⓑ A wolf is smarter than a spider.
   ⓒ A wolf is like a spider.
   ⓓ No mistake.

4. ⓔ Among a cow, dog, and squirrel, a cow has the biggest brain.
   ⓕ Among a cow, dog, and squirrel, a cow has the bigger brain.
   ⓖ Among a cow, dog, and squirrel, a cow has brain.
   ⓗ No mistake.

---

Mrs. Porter lives next door. She has a friend. <u>I hear her call out to him</u>
<u>morning</u>. They have a good time. <u>His name is Perry and he talks</u>. He
(5)                                          (6)
has shiny feathers of bright red and green. Many people have a parrot
like Perry.

**5.** ⓐ I hear her call out to him every morning.

ⓑ I hear her call out to him.

ⓒ I hear her call out to him last morning.

ⓓ No mistake.

**6.** ⓔ His name is Perry and he is talk.

ⓕ His name is Perry and he talks loudly.

ⓖ His name is Perry and he is loud.

ⓗ No mistake.

---

The animals that live in Australia are unusual. <u>There are kangaroos. The</u>
<u>kangaroos are large</u>. In the northern swamps, there are fierce crocodiles.
                                                        (7)
<u>Sometimes you hear a dingo howl. It howls sadly.</u>
                    (8)

**7.** ⓐ There are kangaroos and are large.

ⓑ There are large kangaroos.

ⓒ There are kangaroos. They are large.

ⓓ No mistake.

**8.** ⓔ Sometimes you hear a dingo howl sadly.

ⓕ Sometimes you hear a dingo.

ⓖ Sometimes you hear a dingo. It howls.

ⓗ No mistake.

---